What About Pete?

Betty Price

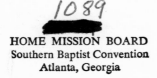

HOME MISSION BOARD
Southern Baptist Convention
Atlanta, Georgia

COVER ART: Alan Tiegreen

What About Pete?

1089

CONTENTS

What About Pete?

1

"WOW! SUNSET STRIP!" FOURTEEN-YEAR-OLD SUSIE was breathless, her head thrust out the back window and her short hair whipping madly around her face. It was just long enough to blow into her eyes where it drove her contact lenses crazy.

"Is it what you expected?" Mrs. Patton wanted to know.

"I don't know. I guess I thought it would be all movie stars and nightclubs. I didn't know there were office buildings." She looked at the Playboy Club rising just above them and then at the tall 9000 Sunset Building in the distance, with neon numerals "9000" emblazoned across the top of the building.

"No place looks very glamorous and romantic in broad daylight. Wait till dark," said Rod, Susie's seventeen-year-old brother. He sat beside her in the back seat and casually glanced out the window. He wanted to appear nonchalant. Susie could gawk like a tourist, but not him.

"Daddy," said Susie, "there's an ice cream place. Please can we stop?"

"That's probably the best idea I've heard all day,"

1

said Mr. Patton. "Traffic on the streets is almost as bad as the freeways," he muttered, watching the other lane over his shoulder. He had to wait for four cars to pass before he could ease into the right lane and then into a parking place along the curb near Wil Wright's Ice Cream Parlor.

"What are Rosicrucians, Daddy?" asked Susie, getting out of the car.

"What are what?"

"See that sign," she said, pointing toward the building they had parked in front of.

The display window of the building next to Wil Wright's contained a poster announcing a meeting of the group.

"I don't know what it is," Mr. Patton said, after scanning the main headlines. "Sounds like some strange kind of religion."

"Let's go find out," Susie said curiously, already starting for the front door.

"No, come here," Mr. Patton stated with the conviction of a man who knows the sound of his voice is enough.

Susie stopped immediately on hearing the tone of his voice and giggled.

"Oh, Daddy, where's your sense of adventure?" she teased.

Rod was still standing in front of the Rosicrucian sign, reading the fine print.

"Thinking of becoming a—whatever that is?" Susie asked.

"Rosicrucian? No, but I think it's interesting all the strange things people believe."

"Do you two want any ice cream?" their father asked.

They headed for Wil Wright's. A little bell jingled as they opened the door.

"Hi, be right with you," yelled a tall, slender boy

behind the counter. He was stooped over a hot fudge sundae onto which he was spooning lots of whipped cream.

"Order whatever you want," Mr. Patton said.

"I'll have the secret flavor," said Susie, peering over the counter for a glimpse into the mysterious cardboard container labeled: "Secret Flavor of the Month."

"Make mine a double chocolate almond," Rod ordered.

"Where are you guys from anyway?" grinned the boy behind the counter as he dipped his ice cream scoop into Susie's surprise flavor.

"We're from—" Susie started when Rod interrupted.

"What makes you think we aren't native Californians?" he asked.

He chuckled. "That's probably the funniest question I've heard all week. First of all, if you had been in California more than twenty-four hours, you would know there's practically no such animal as a native Californian. Everyone comes from somewhere else. And sometimes I think it's only the weird ones who come here. No offense intended—I came here from Philadelphia myself. And second, if you could hear yourself talk the way I hear you, you wouldn't ask that question either." He looked at Susie, batted his eyelashes twice and said, "Y'all come, h-o-n-e-y c-h-i-l-e." He imitated her heavy drawl, then laughed at how well he did it.

"Are our accents really that strong?" asked Rod seriously.

" 'Fraid so. Bet that's your wagon out there with all the luggage."

"That's right," said Rod.

"Georgia?"

"No, but you're close. Texas; and Arkansas before that."

"I thought so. On vacation?"

"No, the family just moved here. My dad got transferred," Rod said.

"What line of work?"

"Accounting."

"Must be a big shot to get moved to California."

"He's the company vice-president."

The boy behind the counter looked impressed.

Continuing their drive down Sunset Strip, the Pattons stopped at the traffic light at San Vicente. The whiskey-a-go-go on the opposite corner advertised "Dusty and Sweets McGee" on a full-size billboard covering one wall of the building. The 9000 Building was in full view now. A group of young people wearing full-length white robes and sandals was crossing the street. Most of them had shaved their heads and wore a funny-looking pigtail hanging from the back of their heads. They were singing and playing strange musical instruments. A girl was shaking a tambourine.

Susie wondered who they were and what they were doing, but no one in the car knew. The group disappeared down the hill to their left. Mrs. Patton remarked that it was the strangest thing she had ever seen.

"There sure are a lot of nude nightclubs here," Susie commented, watching the signs on the clubs. "Rod, have you ever been to a nude place?"

"Of course not, silly," said Rod, embarrassed. "When would I have ever gone to a nude club? And why?"

"I don't know. I just wondered what it would be like." Her thoughts were already off in the other world of her imagination, so Rod just let the subject drop.

A few minutes later they pulled up in front of the Benedict Canyon house that Mr. Patton had rented two weeks earlier when he flew to Los Angeles to make the final arrangements for their move.

"Oh, it's a lovely house. It really is," Mrs. Patton beamed. Susie and Rod exchanged glances in the back seat and shrugged. Their mother had hated leaving her home in Texas, and they both expected her to dislike thoroughly whatever California house they moved into.

It was certainly bigger than any house they had lived in before. The four bedrooms meant there was an extra room for work space for everybody. The living room was huge with high, beamed ceilings and a rock fireplace at one end. The shag carpet was green and deep.

"Oh, take your shoes off. Doesn't that feel yummy?" Susie purred.

The kitchen was wood-paneled with modern built-ins. In the den, Susie gasped, "Oooh, look." Through the sliding glass doors was a swimming pool. That was the surprise. Rod and Susie couldn't believe it.

"Dad, that's really great," Rod said, finding it difficult to be nonchalant about having a swimming pool right in your own backyard.

"Wow. Oh, wow! Daddy, I just can't believe it. Why didn't you tell us? What a marvelous surprise. Oh, thank you, Daddy." Susie was beside herself as she gave her father a crushing bear hug. Determined to be the first one in the pool, she rushed off to change clothes.

"Wait," called Mrs. Patton. "Let's unload the car first."

"Aw, Mom," Susie's voice was muffled behind the door of her new bedroom. "It'll be easier to work if we cool off first."

Mrs. Patton gave up with a shrug of exasperation. Except for details like a kitchen cabinet affixed in an awkward spot, a wall that was two inches too short to accommodate her favorite bookcase and the shape of the bathtub, she was unusually pleased with their California home. And the swimming pool did give the house an added something which their home in Texas didn't have.

"Come on, Rod, last one in gets to unload the car!"

"No way, little sister. You don't get out of it that easy."

Rod and Susie swam till they were exhausted. They enjoyed the pool as though they couldn't believe it would be there for them the next day. They had to rest from the exercise before they could unload the car.

When Rod went out to begin carrying luggage in, he found an advertisement circular on the windshield. "Buddhist meeting tonight—and every Tuesday night at 7:30 P.M., Public Invited." The ad included a map showing how to get to the address, which was only a couple of blocks from their house.

"Susie, you're not gonna believe this," Rod shouted as Susie slammed the front door behind her.

"What?"

"We live practically next door to some Buddhists."

"You're kidding!" she said, her curiosity up.

"See for yourself." He handed her the paper and began untying a couple of suitcases from the top of the wagon.

"Hi." They turned to greet a girl with long, straight blonde hair. She was probably about sixteen, Rod judged.

"Hi," they said together.

"New around here?" she asked.

"Just got here today," Rod answered.

"Why don't you come to our meeting," she asked, pointing to the sheet in Susie's hand.

"Are you a Buddhist?" Susie tried to hide her awe.

"Sure am." The other girl smiled. "What religion are you guys?"

"Er—we're Christians," Rod said.

"Real Christians or just church people?" she asked.

Rod was startled. He had never been asked that question before.

"Real Christians, I hope," he said. "Of course, where we come from, real Christians go to church."

"What I've found in chanting is better than anything my Christian friends tell me about. Yesterday morning I got up and chanted for some shoes 'cause I didn't have any. I had to go to San Diego, and three hours later the woman who lives next door to us came over with a pair of shoes she was about to throw away. She just happened to think someone here might need them. And you wanna hear something really wild? They were exactly my size!"

Rod and Susie were really taken aback. It sounded like the kind of testimonies Christians often gave in their church.

Finally he said, "Yeah, that really is wild."

"Of course, you can probably do things like that with Jesus too. He and Buddha were both prophets, you know," she conceded.

"Yeah, but not in the same way," Rod began.

"Why not?" the girl asked flippantly.

"Well, Jesus was the Son of God," Rod stated, but his voice didn't sound too confident.

"So are we all, my friend," she said happily.

Rod felt anger welling up within him. He felt as though he had been put on the defensive, and he didn't know why.

"Not the same way Jesus was," Rod said.

"So what's the difference?"

"Well, first of all, Jesus was unique. He was born of a virgin."

She laughed.

Rod couldn't believe it.

"Listen, this is California in the twentieth century." The girl sounded so sure of herself. "You've got to come up with something better than that. Everybody thinks Jesus was a groovy dude. Why don't you just accept that?"

"Because there's something wrong with it," Rod said, restraining his anger and frustration.

"What?"

"I don't know right offhand—"

"Well, I tell you what: when you get your argument together—a good logical, twentieth-century argument —you come to one of our Buddhist meetings, and we'll talk about it." Her tone was condescending. "Bye now." She walked off down the driveway.

"Rod, let's go to their meeting," Susie said. She was intrigued by the whole thing.

"Not tonight; maybe next week."

"Oh, Rod, why can't we go tonight?" she begged.

"Susie, we just got here. Be practical for once. We need to unpack and get settled. There'll be plenty of time to go to Buddhist meetings later." Her brother started up the sidewalk, tripped on one of the rocks that separated it from the flower garden, and dropped a blue suitcase which decapitated three violets.

Susie giggled. "You're all brains and practicality— and no grace. Okay, but next week for sure can we visit our Buddhist neighbors? Promise?"

"No, I don't promise. I said maybe." Rod was angry at himself for stumbling. He grabbed the suitcase and started up the sidewalk again.

When the car was unloaded, they both returned to the pool. Susie slid down the sliding board into the shallow end, swam six lengths of the pool and threw herself down exhausted on a towel next to her brother. He was staring off into space.

"Rod, do you believe what that girl said?"

"About what?"

"You know, about the shoes?"

"Why shouldn't I?"

"Well, does God answer the Buddhists when they chant? I mean, I always thought Christianity was the only way. But if that's true, why do they get answers to their prayers?"

"There's probably a reasonable explanation," he said gruffly.

"Oh, Rod, why don't you just admit you don't know and that you're angry because you don't have an answer?"

"Why don't you just leave me alone? If you're so smart, you figure it out, Miss Psychiatrist." He got up and dove into the pool.

The next day he washed and waxed the car. He felt sure they must have brought half the California desert with them. The inside curves of the bumpers were piled high with sand and dirt.

"Need some help?" A boy about Rod's age was walking up the driveway. He wore jeans and a T-shirt with several small holes in the front of it. His brown hair was below his ears.

"Well, uh, I guess so," Rod said hesitantly. He'd never heard California was a particularly friendly place, and he certainly didn't expect neighborly hospitality. But here stood a guy about his own age with a pleasant smile on his face.

"Name's Pete," he said, holding out his hand.

"I'm Rod. Thanks for the help." He shook hands.

"Anytime. Why don't I start drying." Pete grabbed a chamois and went to the rear of the car which Rod had already washed. Lightly he began to wipe away the droplets of water which the sun was already drying.

"You live around here?" Rod asked, speaking over the noise of the hose.

"Yeah, down the block. I was across the street trying to round up my brother Andy, but he and his friend have gone off somewhere. Probably to the drags at Riverside. Mom will be mad—she wanted him home in time for dinner," Pete said. "Where're you from?"

"Texas."

"I suspected as much." Pete grinned.

"You from California?"

"Nope. Missouri."

"How long have you lived here?" Rod asked.

"About six years. My dad lost his job in Missouri, so we came to California looking for the rainbow or the pot of gold or whatever people come to California for." Pete scrubbed the headlights thoughtfully.

"Did you find it?"

"Does anyone? No, you can't ever run away. My dad's just not making it—here *or* Missouri."

Hearing the bitterness in Pete's voice, Rod glanced at him. His face was tight and he was glaring at the damp spot which he was rubbing furiously. Rod started to wax the car. "Is your dad working?" he asked.

Pete had almost finished drying.

"Is your dad working?" Rod asked again.

"Sometimes. Construction jobs here and there," Pete said. "What about your dad?"

"He's an accountant. He was transferred here," Rod answered.

"Maybe he'll find the rainbow. It's easier when you start out with a pot of gold." Pete sounded cynical.

"How old are you, Pete?"

"Seventeen. And you?"

"The same. Senior?"

"Yeah. Listen, I'm sorry to leave before you're finished, but Mom's expecting me for dinner," Pete said. He gave a swipe to the last streak of water and carelessly tossed the chamois onto the rim of the water bucket.

"Wanta go down to Bob's with me tonight?"

"Bob's? Who's he?"

"That's Bob's Big Boy on Ventura Boulevard, a hamburger place where most of the kids hang out. You can meet some of them."

"Okay. What time?"

"I'll pick you up at seven thirty. Be ready. I'll just honk." Pete was off at a half-run down the street.

"Hey, thanks," Rod shouted after him. Pete turned halfway around and waved without slowing down.

At seven thirty it was dark, and the cars were bumper-to-bumper on Ventura Boulevard. Pete had the top down on his '67 green convertible, and the night air was cool. Rod watched the neon signs, the empty storefronts and the flashy restaurants as they drove slowly by.

On the dashboard was a small plastic Madonna. Rod was a little surprised. It had not occurred to him that Pete might be Catholic, but then it had not occurred to him to wonder about Pete's religion at all. Occasionally Rod glanced at Pete. He seemed very sure of himself. Lounging back in his seat, his left elbow rested on the window and his right hand rested on his leg with the thumb casually hooked over the bottom of the steering wheel. Whenever he saw someone he knew, he pounded on his car horn until they turned to wave. He laughed loudly and shouted flip comments into the windows of passing cars.

He's showing off for me, Rod thought. Pete hadn't acted like that during the afternoon. Rod had appreciated Pete's taking an interest in him, and now he felt a small resentment. He tried to ignore it. What more could he ask than to make a friend his second day in California?

Pete obviously had lots of friends, and he seemed to enjoy having an attentive audience right now. It seemed just a little rude for Pete to pay so much attention to people in other cars. Rod wanted to be a friend, not a fan. But he also knew that some of his feelings stemmed from a slight jealousy. He had never been able to be as outgoing and easy with people as Pete was.

Rod felt generally estranged and uncomfortable in the whole situation. He struggled with a sudden impulse to get out of the car at the next stoplight and try to find his way home walking, but he forced the thought out of his mind. Making new friends had never been easy for him. He did okay once he got to know people and felt comfortable with them. But the getting-acquainted period was always terrible. Usually, if he were patient, it would soon pass.

The evening was much like the past two days had been, filled with strange new people, places, and experiences. It was a world of smog, traffic, houses with swimming pools, Rosicrucians, Buddhists, freeways and people in strange white robes.

"Rod, meet Al, Joe and Cynthia," Pete said with his arm on Rod's shoulder as they walked into Bob's. Rod shook hands with the guys and nodded at the girl. She was wearing the shortest skirt he had ever seen.

"Hey, can we join you?" Pete asked, again very confidently.

"Sure, Pete," Al said. "The more, the merrier."

The waitress motioned for them and led the way to a table in the back. Rod glanced around as they walked through the room. The place was filled with young people—some dates and some groups. Pete waved at several kids as they passed by. They were seated in a large round booth.

"Hey, where's Scott tonight?" Pete asked.

"He and Blanche and Joey and somebody else went to Marshall's to turn on. His parents are out of town for the weekend."

"Right on!" Pete grinned mischievously.

Suddenly, in a move Rod decided later was calculated to put him on the spot, Pete turned to him casually and asked, "You ever turn on, Rod?" All eyes turned to him.

"What do you mean?" Rod asked after an awkward hesitation.

"You know, man. You ever smoke grass?" Pete said.

"Marijuana?"

"Of course, marijuana." Rod noticed Cynthia grinning. He was embarrassed. There was nothing to do except be honest and let them think whatever they wanted to.

"No," he said. They were all grinning. Rod wished he were dead. And it was even worse because they didn't say anything; they just grinned at each other for what seemed an endless period of time.

Finally somebody said, "Did you see Hal's new car?" And they all changed their attention to a new subject, but Rod didn't hear a word they said. He sat there numb, praying that they would break up and leave soon. He was ashamed of their disdain, but he was even more ashamed that he hadn't spoken up in his own defense. There were perfectly good reasons why he shouldn't smoke marijuana. He should have presented his case casually and not cared what they thought. But he had just sat there, cowed by them. He had not offered a single reason for his behavior and belief.

Susie was waiting up for him when he got home.

"Hey, it's the man about town," she whispered loudly as he passed her open door. But he walked right by without even slowing down.

She got out of bed and followed him to his room.

"What's wrong with you?" she asked lightly.

"Nothing." He was looking for his pajamas in the third drawer of the chest, and he wouldn't look at her.

"Hey, you got to go out and meet people the second

night you're in California. What more could you ask for?"

"Susie, I don't want to talk about it. Go away and leave me alone." He was straining to control his voice.

She turned to leave and then tried once more. "Rod, sometimes it helps to talk about—"

"Shut up—and get out!" He threw the pajama top across the room at her. It flew up into the air and dropped to the floor a couple of feet in front of him.

She retreated quickly.

2

SOME OF THE PATTON'S FURNITURE DID NOT ARRIVE
until the second week after they moved into their house.
Unfortunately, one of the late items was the washing
machine. Toward the end of the week Mrs. Patton
gave up expecting it to arrive. She piled all their dirty
clothes into three big laundry hampers and gave Susie
the job of doing them at the laundromat. Rod drove
her to the nearest one and helped her get everything
loaded into the machines before he left to run an er-
rand for his dad.

Susie sat down in the lounge area of the laundromat
and sorted through the magazines on the table beside
her—*Time, Life, Glamour* and *Watchtower,* the Jehovah's witness publication. She picked up an out-
dated copy of *Glamour* and flipped through it, paying
careful attention to the fashion section. Finally, she
dropped the magazine and glanced around the room.

An overweight, middle-aged woman in old gray
shorts and a shocking pink T-shirt was dumping her
clothes out of a cart into a dryer. Her hair was in rollers
and her feet were stuck into ragged pink bedroom
slippers. Susie grimaced and said to herself, "I'll never
look like that."

Two skinny guys about twenty-five-years-old were folding their laundry at a table on the other side of the room. They looked too dressed up to be at a laundromat. They were both wearing tight pants and see-through flowered shirts. There was something a little effeminate about them. "Not my type," Susie dismissed them.

"Hey, weigh those clothes first," the laundry manager shouted at a woman who was throwing clothes into a dry cleaning machine. "They can't be over eight pounds, lady, and I have to see them on the scales. Too many people overload the machines and bust 'em."

The exasperated woman obviously clenched her jaws and began to remove the clothes from the machine without saying a word. In an angry gesture she threw them onto the scale, and a yellow blouse fell to the floor. The manager leaned over to pick it up, but she leaped to his side and jerked it away. She dropped it on the scale.

"See, lady, two pounds over. I knew it," the manager said.

They continued wrangling while Susie picked up the *Watchtower* magazine. One article quoted from "The Truth that Leads to Eternal Life," the handbook of the Jehovah's witnesses:

For thousands of years men of faith have lived in eager expectation of the day when God's kingdom would begin its rule. They have felt keenly the need for God to take a direct hand in earth's affairs. Does this mean that God has not been King during the centuries past? No, for Jehovah has always been the Supreme Ruler of the universe. But here at the earth his rulership has been challenged. . . . All the foretold marks of the "last days" are here. They prove beyond a doubt that we have been in the "last days" since 1914. Hence it was in that year that God's heavenly kingdom came to power!

"That's ridiculous," Susie said to herself, tossing the magazine aside and looking around the room again. Two little blond-haired twin boys were racing out the back door with a metal laundry cart. The manager saw them and went flying out the door and across the parking lot after them. Susie had been to a laundromat in Texas only once that she remembered, but she certainly didn't remember the people being so weird. Must be 'cause it's California, she decided.

Just about the time she had given up hope of seeing some young people her own age, a guy and girl entered together, both teen-agers. The guy was really good-looking and Susie wished he were alone. She watched them put their clothes into the washer. The girl, who was short and petite, went to the manager to get change, and the boy wandered in Susie's direction. She quickly lowered her gaze again to the magazine table.

"Hi," he said as he reached for the *Time* and dropped into the seat on the other side of the table.

"Hi," Susie said, smiling.

At the sound of her voice, the boy looked at her a second time. "Hey, where are you from?" he asked, grinning.

Susie restrained herself from getting angry.

"Texas," she answered, shortly.

"Sorry. I didn't mean to make fun of you. I like your drawl. It was just so unexpected. Forgive me?"

"Okay." Susie couldn't think of anything witty to say.

"How long have you been in California?"

"One week," she said.

"Well, no wonder you still have your drawl. You'll lose it if you stay here long," he said, smiling at her.

"I don't really want to. But I don't like being laughed at either," Susie said.

"I can imagine that's unpleasant. And again, I'm sorry."

"Okay, it's okay."

"My name's Richard," he said and held out his hand. Susie didn't remember shaking hands with a boy her age before, but she took his hand. Besides, he seemed a little older. He was even more handsome when he smiled. He had black hair, and he wore glasses with heavy dark frames. They made him look sophisticated and smart.

"I'm Susie."

"I'm happy to meet you." The girl suddenly walked up beside him, and he looked up. "Hey, meet my sister Ann. This is Susie."

The girls exchanged greetings. That was better. She was only his sister.

When Susie left the laundromat an hour later, she knew that Richard was eighteen and a senior at the school where she would be a freshman, that his sister Ann was two years older than herself, and that they were both coming to the Pattons' house the next day for a swim. She also knew they were Jewish, and she had never had any Jewish friends before.

When they came, Susie and Rod with their guests wasted no time getting into the pool.

"Try the diving board. It's great," Susie shouted to Richard. He walked out to the end of the board, gave it two light, trial springs and did a beautiful half-gainer. Susie waited for him to surface.

"Hey, I didn't know you were professional," she called.

"Not professional. But I used to go to camp every summer," he said, laughing.

"Hey, Pete's here," Rod said, looking up as Pete came through the sliding glass doors.

"Hi, everybody," Pete waved. Rod introduced him to Richard and Ann.

Rod had mixed feelings about Pete. He still felt a little uncomfortable around him after the whole scene about smoking pot. He secretly blamed Pete for getting him into that embarrassing situation, but Pete's response had been unexpected. Rod thought Pete would write him off as a naive kid from Texas who just wasn't as sophisticated as his California pals. But Pete continued to call and to come around. At first, Rod thought maybe he was interested in Susie, but later it became obvious that he wasn't. He seemed to like Rod, so Rod tried to be friends with him and wondered what it all meant.

Pete wore a handsome swimsuit of madras checks, and around his neck was a St. Christopher medal. The way he puffed his cigarette added to his air of sophistication. He was a nice-looking guy, but Susie obviously liked Richard better, Rod thought as he watched them together.

Later, as they all waited for hot dogs at the pool side, Susie said, "I just thought of something, Rod. You know what we could do tonight after the hot dogs?"

"What?" Rod responded, looking up from his conversation with Pete.

"Tonight is the night of that Buddhist meeting, and we could all go." Her eyes were dancing with anticipation.

"Oh, I don't think so—"

"Why not, man? Might be a wild scene. Just for kicks, man," Pete said. He sounded as anxious as Susie for adventure.

"Well, whatever everyone wants," Rod agreed reluctantly. Susie called to the other side of the pool where Richard was sunning and Ann was throwing water on him.

"Richard, would you like to go to a Buddhist meeting tonight, just to see what it's like?"

"To a Buddhist meeting?"

"Yeah, they're having one just down the street, and Rod and I thought it would be fun—"

"Hey, *you* thought," Rod stopped her.

"Oh, okay, I think it would be fun and Rod has to be persuaded," Susie corrected herself. "Let's all go."

"Well, I don't know."

"Sounds fascinating," Ann said.

"I think it's a great idea," Pete said. "Come on, Rod, it'll be interesting, and no one can get hurt."

"What do you think, Richard?" Rod asked.

"I wouldn't mind observing what they do," he said, "if they won't pressure us into participating."

"Oh, they won't. Come on, Rod," Susie tried to persuade her brother.

"Okay, just to make it unanimous. At least we're close enough to home that anyone can come back anytime he wants to," Rod agreed.

"I bet you'll be first," Susie teased.

They roasted hot dogs on a grill beside the pool and ate them with baked beans and Mrs. Patton's special potato salad which everyone bragged on. Then they all scrambled off to almost every room in the house to change clothes and to dry their hair.

The six of them arrived at the Buddhist meeting shortly after it had begun. As they walked up the driveway of the little Spanish-style house, they heard monotone chanting. The sound created a humming effect as if a musical instrument was accompanying them.

"Oh, listen," whispered Susie.

"Man, that's weird," Pete said.

"I'm not sure we should be here." Rod was having second thoughts about having agreed to come.

"Oh, silly, come on," Susie chided.

When no one answered the doorbell, probably because they couldn't hear it, Pete opened the front door and they entered quietly. Just inside the hallway various shoes were spread on the floor—sandals, boots, thongs, wooden cloppers. Pete whipped off his boots, laid them beside the others and started toward the room where he heard the chanting. The others followed a little more slowly.

Here apparently was the Buddhists' room for worship. About fifteen people with their backs to the door were on their knees on the floor. They held their hands together in a folded, prayerful position, and most of them had a string of beads wrapped around their hands. Occasionally they would rub the beads together, giving an even more eerie sound to their chanting. They seemed to be chanting the same words over and over and over again, sometimes slowly and sometimes much faster. The words were foreign, probably Chinese or Japanese, and it was strange to hear such a chant from these people, all of whom appeared to be Americans.

Pete led the way for the group, and they sat on the floor a little way back from the chanters.

The room contained only three chairs. Rod wondered if it had any more furniture than that and if it had just been moved out for the meeting. Displayed on the wall were a couple of pictures of an Oriental man and several charts which seemed to represent a system for dividing up the city. *Probably their evangelistic outreach strategy,* Rod thought. But the most unusual aspect of the room was the thing to which these people were chanting. It looked like some kind of Oriental altar with tiny pictures and odd-looking vessels and an incense burner. There was even a banana on the altar. Hanging on the wall above the altar was a frame containing a scroll with some Chinese-looking writing on it. The chanters formed a reverent semi-circle around the altar and scroll.

All of the people in the room were young, aging probably from eighteen to thirty. Two children romped quietly about the room, occasionally upturning objects which caused their parents to run after them and right everything before returning to their chanting. Several of the chanters turned to nod and smile as the six curious newcomers sat down at the back of the room.

The chanting continued for about half an hour. The worshipers remained in their same position throughout the service except for a few times when all together they bowed over until their faces touched the floor. One guy seemed like sort of a leader because he would sometimes chant alone or begin a chant in which the others would join. Some chanted by following along in a little book; others obviously knew the whole ceremony without having to look at the book. Finally, they chanted the words very slowly and prayerfully, and then a little bell rang from somewhere. They all sat up and formed a circle. The spell created by the chanting was broken. They seemed like ordinary people now as they laughed and talked.

"Hey, we have some guests," said the man who was probably the leader. He motioned to them. "You guys move up closer. Welcome to our meeting."

Susie and Rod and their friends scooted a little closer to the chanters' circle.

"This is a meeting of *Nichiren Shoshu,*" the leader explained. "The main thing is we chant to get benefits in our lives. We chant to the *Gohonzon* which is the scroll on the wall, and we get what we chant for. Each one of us has a *Gohonzon* in our own home." He looked around the group. "Who would like to tell us about a benefit you have received this week?"

A tall, slender guy with long hair raised his hand and stood up. The group applauded happily for him.

"I'm Frank, and I've been practicing Buddhism for six months. I got a great benefit this week. At least, it was great to me. I'm a musician, see, and I hadn't had any confidence in myself for several years until I started practicing Buddhism. And now everything's changed. I get gigs all the time, and I'm not afraid I'll fail. And I'm getting better all the time.

"Now last week I had this session in a recording studio, and I chanted *daimoku* for half an hour before I went to the session. I did so good they wanted me to come back the next day for twice as much money. And everything's been like that since I started practicing. I started telling this other guy in the session with me, and he wants to come next week and start chanting with us." He sat down, and the group applauded again.

A little blonde girl raised her hand and stood, and everyone applauded again. Rod and Susie suddenly recognized her as the girl who had invited them to the meeting.

"I've really been getting lots of benefits lately. I just have so much to do—what with my job, our activities here, getting ready for the district Buddhist convention and taking care of my mother who just had an operation. So I've been chanting, and I keep fighting and I'm really winning."

Then speaking toward the guests, she said, "You see, it's no good to fight and lose. Lots of people do that. That's one of the main benefits of practicing—we fight and win. My attitude about so many things is changing. Sometimes I don't even know what to chant for, but I chant anyway, and pretty soon the *Gohonzon* tells me what to chant for. It's great." She sat down amidst the applause.

A handsome guy about thirty got up next. "I'm an ad salesman for a Hollywood company, and I've always been a sort of playboy type. A year ago I didn't care about my work. I'd get up in the morning and go out in the backyard and smoke several joints, and I wasn't getting anywhere. You know what I mean? Now I may still go out in the backyard and smoke a joint (The group laughed at that.), but the difference is that after that, I go to work. And I'm making great sales I could never make before. Last week I was chanting for a new car 'cause I really need it, and this week I made enough money on two sales to buy exactly the car I wanted. Wow!"

Everyone laughed with him, as though they were having similar experiences.

"Okay," said the leader. "What about announcements? Chris?"

"We're having a picnic here Saturday afternoon. Everyone's invited. And bring guests. You'll get more information on time and what to bring later this week in the mail," said a girl who must have been Chris.

"This sounds like a pretty neat outfit," Pete whispered to Rod. "It's not at all what I expected. When they stop that weird chanting stuff, they seem like regular guys."

Rod just frowned.

"We'll have a question-and-answer time if anyone, guests or members, has any questions," the leader said.

When no one responded, the leader turned to the group in the back. "Have you guys ever been to a chanting meeting before?"

"No," Pete spoke up.

"Then some of you probably have questions," the leader said. "Don't be hesitant."

"I do." It was Susie. "I never even saw a Buddhist before in my life." Everyone laughed. "Why do you chant?"

"Well, chanting increases our vital life force. It gives us more energy. *Nam*, the first word of our chant, is like the true name of life. You might say it is the true name for God. Chanting is evoking this life force or life condition to appear in your life."

"Why do you have to keep repeating it out loud over and over again?" Pete wanted to know.

"You can't just think it, because thoughts can't really be measured. You speak it because sound can be measured and recorded."

"Are you chanting to a higher Being?" asked Richard.

"To the *Gohonzon,* which is a mirror to reflect your life within just as other mirrors reflect the outside of your body. It's a mirror of your self."

"Do you see your inner self through your own efforts or with the help of a supernatural power?" Richard went on.

"Well, it's sort of both," the leader said.

"Do you get anything from chanting besides material things?" Richard seemed interested, but mostly out of an intellectual curiosity.

"Oh, yeah, like Mike here who gained confidence as a musician. The greatest benefits are not material; they are a change in character."

"You mean people really do change?" Richard asked.

"They sure do. Everyone of us has changed."

"Is it the power of positive thinking?" asked Richard.

"That's part of it," the leader admitted. "Our minds have fantastic powers we haven't begun to discover yet."

"What about the Four Noble Truths and the Eight-fold Path?" Richard asked.

"Hey, I'm impressed," Susie whispered.

The Buddhist leader evidently was, too. He looked at Richard with new respect in his face. "Oh, we don't believe in them," he explained. "Gautama Buddha, through intensive study and meditation for about forty years, became enlightened. He then gathered a group of disciples about him and taught them his doctrine of self-enlightenment. After forty years of this teaching, he told these disciples that after two thousand years his teachings would be of no value. He predicted that at that time another Buddha would come."

The man paused a moment, then went on. "Nichiren Daishonin taught that allegiance to Amida Buddha is the one true religion. The new Buddha said that the essence of the other Buddha's teaching was found in the titles of his studies. *Nam myoho renge kyo* represents those titles. The old teachings really don't apply to modern man. They're more for people who want to be monks. Nichiren taught that we should overcome our problems rather than try to escape from them."

"What's the difference between Zen and what you believe?" Richard wanted to know. It was obvious he had done some reading on Buddhism.

"Well, Zen is a philosophy of detachment from life. It's escape. Like I said, we believe in overcoming our problems, not in escaping them." The Buddhist paused. "Why don't we close our meeting," he said to the whole group, "and then we can continue to discuss these things informally, if you want to. We always invite our guests to say the chant with us if they would like to. Do some of you want to?"

Susie was wide-eyed and nodding. Ann watched Richard to see what he would do. Richard and Rod looked straight at the leader and shook their heads.

"Okay, here's how you say it for those of you who want to try. *Nam myoho renge kyo*. Practice it one time," the leader encouraged them.

As the chanters pronounced the strange syllables, Susie and Pete joined them while Richard, Ann and Rod only listened. Rod was visibly distressed that Susie was participating. The chanters turned again to face the Gohonzon and gave their closing chant. Then the official part of the meeting broke up.

The leader, the blonde girl who had invited them and another girl joined them. The leader, a man named Paul, began telling Pete how he could join the chanters if he wanted to. The other girl, who was a district chairman named Sherry, shared her chanting experiences with Ann, and the blonde girl made straight for Rod where he was talking with Richard and Susie.

"Well, hi, Christian," she practically shouted across the room. The name sounded derogatory coming from her. Several of the chanters around the room turned to look, and Rod felt hot with embarrassment.

"Hi," he said when she got closer. His voice sounded tight, even to him.

"Done anymore research on Jesus since I saw you?" she asked, smiling condescendingly. Rod didn't say anything; he just looked uncomfortable.

Suddenly the girl's attitude changed. "I'm sorry. I sound like a real smart aleck, don't I? I really am glad you came," she said.

"Thanks," Rod said, trying to be friendly.

"By the way, my name's Pat," she said, and they all exchanged introductions. "Are all of you Christians?" she asked.

"No. My sister and I are Jewish," Richard said.

"Have you studied Buddhism?"

"Not really. I've always been interested in world religions, and I've done some reading on the subject," he explained.

Pat nodded. "I have more respect for a person who tells me his way is right if he's tried the other ways or at least knows something about them." She glanced briefly in Rod's direction, then returned her gaze to Richard. "Do you believe your way is right?"

"Of course." Richard grinned, and no one could tell if he spoke with his tongue in cheek.

"Are you an Orthodox Jew?"

"No. Reformed."

"Do you go to temple?"

"Yes."

After a while Rod suggested that they go back to the house for another swim, so they found their right shoes and got them on. When they were outside, Susie was the first to speak. "That was really wild. I never saw anything like that before."

"You're right. It's different," Richard said.

Back beside the pool again, Rod asked Richard what were the things he had asked about that the Buddhist leader said they didn't believe in.

"The Four Noble Truths and the Eightfold Path?"

"Yeah."

"Well, they're the basis for the oldest or the most pure form of Buddhism," Richard told him. "The Four Noble Truths are, first, that human existence is filled with suffering; second, that the cause of the suffering is a craving for the alluring things of this world; third, that the suffering can be stopped; and, fourth, that the way to end the suffering is through Buddha's Eightfold Path."

"What's that?" Rod asked thoughtfully.

"Right viewpoint, right aspiration, right speech, right behavior, right livelihood, freedom of the individual to determine his own rate of growth toward happiness, right mindfulness and right meditation." Richard had counted on his fingers, trying to remember all eight.

"That's really a handful, isn't it?" Rod commented. "How come you know so much about Buddhism that you can just rattle those things off?"

"Well, I read it sometime ago in my world religion book. Then last week we also got one of those advertisements about the Buddhist meeting, so I got out the book and studied it again. Until tonight I hadn't realized that this Nichiren Shoshu form of Buddhism was so different."

Pete had joined them now. "What did you think of it, Rod?" he wanted to know.

"I never saw anything like it before. I really feel like I'm in a different world here in California. And I got a taste of something else really new to me tonight," Rod said, reflecting.

"What's that?" Richard asked.

"Well, I've never in all my life had someone make fun of me for being a Christian, but I felt like that's what Pat was doing. It was an uncomfortable feeling," he said, "and I don't know how to cope with it."

"Religious groups do that to each other all the time, though. Christians do it, too," Richard said, softly. "Haven't you ever looked down on someone because of what they believed?"

"I don't know. I may have without meaning to. Sometimes I have thought some people believed some pretty stupid things I guess," Rod said.

Richard looked him straight in the eyes. "That's about the same thing. If you let people know that you think what they believe is stupid, then they think you believe they're stupid and that you're rejecting them."

Rob looked startled. "I guess I never thought about that before." He looked soberly across the pool. After a moment he went on. "But I'll have to now. I really felt uncomfortable tonight."

The Pattons joined a small Southern Baptist church in Hollywood near Sunset Strip. Rod and Susie made many friends their own age and were offered plenty of church social activities, if they wanted to participate. The minister was young and particularly interested in teen-agers. He knew how to relate to them, and they liked and respected him. In their church back in Texas the minister had seemed to preach only for adults, and the younger people spent half their time thinking up excuses to miss the services. But here the young people looked forward to going to church, and they usually brought friends with them. It was a pleasant change.

Rod particularly liked Mr. Clark, his Bible teacher in Sunday School, who talked to the boys on their level of interest.

3

ROD AND PETE SPENT MORE AND MORE TIME TO-
gether, and they seemed to have a good influence on
each other. Rod made Pete think before he acted or at
least consider all the alternatives. And Pete challenged
Rod to be a little more outgoing. He continued to intro-
duce him to the local fellows, but now he introduced
Rod as his good friend. Rod forgave him for that first
awkward incident at Bob's Big Boy. He came to understand that Pete had acted the way he did to be "in" with
the gang. Now that he had a friend in Rod, he didn't
seem to need the approval of the gang as much as he
had.

The two talked about almost everything except their
faith. Several times Rod invited Pete to church with
him, but Pete always refused. He went to mass every
week, but he never said anything about it. Whenever
Rod tried to ask questions, Pete would give a quick
"yes" or "no" and change the subject. He didn't seem
interested in discussing it, so Rod finally gave up.

Then one day it occurred to him it might be interesting to go to mass with Pete. He asked Pete about it.

"Sure, man, it's okay with me," Pete said. He was not enthusiastic but agreeable.

Three weeks before Christmas they went, and Pete volunteered to attend early mass so Rod would not have to miss his own church service.

"But I want to go to the one you usually go to. I want to see the one you like," Rod said.

"They're no different, man. I just go later so I can sleep later. That's all."

"But don't you know a lot of people who go to the one you usually go to?" Rod wanted to know.

"Well, most of the fellows our age go later, but for the same reason I do—so they can sleep later. Listen, man, I don't care. We can go to the later one if you want to."

"Yeah, let's do," Rod said. He dug his hands into his jeans' pockets. "I want to see it the way you do when you go."

Pete shrugged his shoulders. "Okay, okay, man, but it won't be any different."

So they went to the eleven o'clock mass on Sunday morning. The church could hold probably five hundred people, and it wasn't half full. But Rod knew that the church had several masses every Sunday morning whereas his church had only one service in the morning. Pete bent his knee briefly as he entered the pew. The priest was speaking the mass in English, but Rod couldn't understand a word he was saying. He spoke in a singsong chanting fashion which caused his words to slur together. So Rod observed quietly and tried to pick up a word here and there. He followed Pete's lead and knelt on the prayer rail in front of them several times during the mass.

Rod followed the service the best that he could in the "Leaflet Missal" provided in the pew rack. It was sort of a paperback weekly prayer book with the service printed in it. Finally he gave up trying to follow and just read on his own. He was particularly interested in the Liturgy of the Eucharist:

> Blessed are you, Lord, God of all creation.
> Through your goodness we have this bread to offer,
> which earth has given and human hands have made.
> It will become for us the bread of life.
>
> By the mystery of this water and wine
> may we come to share in the divinity of Christ,
> who humbled himself to share in our humanity.
>
> Blessed are you, Lord, God of all creation.
> Through your goodness we have this wine to offer,
> fruit of the vine and work of human hands.
> It will become our spiritual drink.
>
> Lord God, we ask you to receive us
> and be pleased with the sacrifice we offer you
> with humble and contrite hearts.
>
> Lord, wash away my iniquity;
> cleanse me from my sin.

Rod remained seated while Pete went forward to participate in Eucharist, which Rod decided must be the Catholic term for what his church called the Lord's Supper. He watched the people on a couple of pews rise and go forward to kneel at the altar. The priest in his long flowing robes came along with the wafers and the wine. Chanting in words which Rod could not distinguish, he administered them to each person individually. Then they returned to their seats, and the next few pews of people went forward. This procedure continued until everyone in the church had gone forward and received communion.

When the service ended, Pete turned to Rod and said, "Well, what do you think? Different from your church, huh?"

"Yeah, pretty different. Pete," Rod asked, "can you understand what the priest is saying?"

"Sometimes. Mostly it's peaceful just to sit and think."

"You don't really care that you can't understand?"

"Nope. Not really."

"But why do you come?"

"Catholics have to go to mass," Pete said.

"It just doesn't make sense to me to have a guy speaking when you can't understand a word he says."

"Rod, it seems to me if somebody wants to know about other people's religions, he ought to show a real interest and not just be critical. How can you expect someone else to listen to what you say about Jesus unless you respect what he believes in?" Pete asked. He did not really sound angry, but he sounded irritated.

Rod's mouth had dropped open, and he sat there stunned. Then he shoved his hands into his pockets and stared at the toe of his shoe as he quietly kicked the end of the pew.

Pete was embarrassed that he had said as much as he had. "Hey, I didn't mean to sound so grouchy myself," he said.

"It's okay. Let's go," Rod said, getting up. They walked out of the church in strained silence.

Later, in the car Rod finally spoke. "Tell me about your faith and your Church, Pete. I'd really like to know," he said.

Pete glanced over at Rod, but he was staring straight ahead without seeing anything.

"Well, I've believed in Jesus and the Church since I was a little kid, and my folks took me to mass every Sunday. Now I'm a big boy, and I go to mass on my own."

"Do you like to go?"

"It's okay." He shrugged slightly.

"Your Holy Eucharist was different from our Lord's Supper. We believe the bread and the juice are symbols of Christ's body and blood. But I read one time that Catholics believe something different about it," Rod said. His voice was still strained.

"Yeah, we believe the bread and wine actually become the body and blood of Christ," Pete said. "Holy Eucharist is just one of our sacraments."

"What are the others?" Rod asked.

"Baptism, confirmation, penance, marriage, holy orders and extreme unction." He rattled them off somewhat mechanically.

"What's penance?"

"That's when you go to the priest for confession and he absolves you of your sin."

"Why do you have to go to a priest? Can't you confess to God by yourself?"

"Because the priest is God's representative on earth, and the Church says you have to do it that way," Pete answered.

"Do you go to confession?"

"Sure."

"How come you never talk about it?"

"I don't know, man." Pete shrugged and kept his eyes glued to the road.

"Don't you like to talk about it?" he pressed.

"Rod, you're a fanatic. That's why I don't like to talk religion with you." Pete was being frank with great reluctance.

"Pete, you never let on before that you felt that way."

"Well, it wasn't worth losing your friendship to make a big thing of it, and I figured you'd get mad if I said anything."

"Why do you say I'm a fanatic?"

"Because you talk about religion all the time."

"Religion or Jesus?"

"Well, Jesus. You talk about him like he was around all the time."

"But, Pete, shouldn't it be that way? I mean, isn't Jesus around all the time?" Rod asked seriously.

"Well, I guess so, but can't he be there without you talking about him all the time? I mean, people will think you're narrow-minded."

"I don't know. Maybe talking about him means you're aware that he's there. Does that make sense?"

"I guess so, but it still sounds fanatical. Another thing is that it seems like you're getting more fanatical all the time. Why is that?" Pete wanted to know. He looked a little disgusted.

"I'm not sure. But I am understanding my own faith better all the time, and it's becoming more real to me. Remember the first week I got here? I'd never met Buddhists, Rosicrucians, Haré Krishnas and all these other people before, and it scared me. It still does.

He looked out the window as he went on. "I had always thought that all religions except Christianity were way out in left field and there was nothing in them that even remotely resembled truth. When Pat started telling me she got everything she chanted for, she blew my mind. I couldn't explain it, and I guess I felt threatened."

He paused. Pete said nothing, so Rod went on. "I still can't explain all these things and it bugs me. Everytime we have a discussion or an argument, Pat wins. She always has better arguments. It's almost like she knows what I'm going to ask her or what point I'm going to try to prove, and she already has an answer ready. I guess I get frustrated and angry because I can't communicate to her what I *know* to be the truth. And I always have the feeling that she's laughing at me."

"How would Pat know what you're going to ask her? Why does she have all the answers?" Pete asked.

"I don't know. Maybe she's so into Buddhism that she studies it all the time and prepares the right answers ahead of time," Rod guessed.

"Why don't you do that?"

"I wouldn't know where to start, and it would take an awful lot of time."

"But you talk about Jesus all the time. If you're going to do that, you oughta know what you're talking about." Pete looked around quickly. "Hey, I don't mean that for a cut. I'm just trying to understand this whole thing, too. Pat never even *seems* to take me seriously as a Christian."

Rod couldn't wait for Pete to drop him off so he could be alone to think. Pete had really struck a nerve without realizing it. "If you're going to talk about Jesus all the time, you oughta know what you're talking about." Was that his problem? Could he not defend his faith because he didn't know enough about it?

He wandered restlessly around the room, then picked up his Bible and flipped through it. "The Lord is my shepherd, I shall not want." "Blessed are the poor in spirit." "Be ready at all times to give a reason for the hope that is in you." Rod never remembered seeing that particular verse before. *That's exactly what Pete was talking about.* ". . . attaining to all the wealth that comes from the full assurance of understanding, resulting in a true knowledge of God's mystery, that is, Christ Himself, in whom are hidden all the treasures of wisdom and knowledge." Wow! Rod wasn't sure he even understood what that meant, but it sure was heavy. "But if any of you lacks wisdom, let him ask of God, who gives to all men generously and without reproach, and it will be given him." Uhmm.

Rod stared out the window at the swimming pool water which the wind was whipping about gently. He wanted to be able to answer Pat. He wanted to share with Pete how he felt about Jesus. He could read the Bible all the way through and probably read a lot of other books, but it would take at least several years. Pat might not even be around by then, or Pete either. There must be a simpler way—at least to begin.

Rod got up and locked his bedroom door. Then he returned to the bed and dropped on his knees beside it. He knelt there, staring across the bed and out the window for a long time before he spoke. Then finally he bent his head, resting it on his hands.

"God, I'm so confused. I believe you're real but I can't convince anyone else of that. Pat just laughs at me. She doesn't take anything I say seriously. Pete gets angry everytime I try to talk to him. I'm so frustrated and I don't know what to do."

He was silent for a long pause. Then he spoke again. "Please help me, God. I know there's a lot more to know about you than I already know and I want to learn. But I don't know where to start. Lord, what I just read says that you'll give me wisdom if I lack it, and I sure do lack it. Help me to understand. Help me to tell Pat about Jesus. Help me to share more with Pete in love." He stayed on his knees for a while without moving.

Their first Christmas in California was unique—like everything else they found on the West Coast. The weather was cool, but it never got extremely cold the way it did at home. And for some reason that made a big difference. The Pattons had never realized how much they connected the Christmas season with really cold weather. The final straw was driving along the Pacific Coast Highway two weeks before Christmas and seeing one lone surfer out floating on his board. He wore a wetsuit, but Susie was sure she could see goose bumps on his arms all the way from the highway. Nevertheless, there he was the week of December 12 sitting in the ocean on a surfboard. Susie had already been complaining that it didn't seem like Christmas, and that was just too much for her. "He just doesn't realize how selfish he's being. He's calmly sitting out there in the ocean spoiling my Christmas," she pouted good-naturedly. Suddenly she said, "I want it to snow."

"Snow? In California?" Rod looked at her as if she was crazy.

"Yes, it should always snow at Christmas time," she said.

"That's ridiculous. You haven't seen snow at Christmas in years. How come all of a sudden you have to have snow?"

"I think that guy on the surfboard did it. Cold weather isn't enough now—it's got to be snow," she said very seriously and then they both started laughing.

It was a small incident, but it was enough to set Mr. Patton off on planning another surprise. Rod and Susie knew something was going on, but they could not get a word out of their parents about what it was.

Three days before Christmas Mr. Patton loaded everyone into the car with Christmas tree, gift-wrapped packages, cakes and cookies and suitcases full of enough clothes to last a week. They got on the freeway and drove right out of Los Angeles. Rod and Susie were full of curiosity, but they could get nothing out of either parent. Two hours later they were in the mountains and had already hit snow. Susie was wild-eyed.

"I've never seen this much snow anywhere," she exclaimed with awe in her voice.

"This is really fantastic," Rod said.

Three hours out of L. A. they pulled up in front of a four-room cottage Mr. Patton had rented for a week at Big Bear Lake. Susie climbed out of the car.

"This is just unreal. I can't believe it. Oh, thank you, Daddy." Susie threw her arms around her father. Then she grabbed for a snowball and hit Rod on the back of the neck.

"So! You're asking for it, huh?" And he started making his own snowball as Susie ran off down the road. As soon as the snowball was just the right proportion, he took off after her.

That night by the fireplace they trimmed the tree. It was a strange mixture of the contemporary and the traditional. After they had draped on all their modern lights and psychedelic bulbs, Susie wanted to add popcorn and cranberries. She also made and decorated her own favorite Christmas cookies, and they ate every one of them that night.

The next day Mr. Patton took Rod and Susie skiing while Mrs. Patton worked on her special Christmas fruitcake. All three did relatively well considering they had never skied before. Mr. Patton moved about very cautiously and very slowly; he knew he couldn't afford to risk a broken leg or arm. Rod was well-coordinated and fairly graceful. Nevertheless, he was content to spend the entire day on the beginner's slope. Susie was the one who kept wanting to be adventurous, and her father had to hold her down.

"Tomorrow you can come back and that will be soon enough for you to be out on a steeper slope," he said.

Susie grunted, but she was so excited to be actually skiing that she could not complain too much.

After a lovely dinner on Christmas Eve they all sat down in front of the fireplace and beside the tree. Rod read the Christmas story from the second chapter of the Gospel of Luke. Then they went around the family circle and each one of them shared what he especially wanted to thank God for on this Christmas. Mrs. Patton was grateful for her family and how much she loved them. Mr. Patton was grateful that God had given them a safe and happy move to California. Rod was most grateful for Jesus and salvation through him. Susie was grateful for snow and the fact that her parents loved her and Rod so much that they would make Christmas so special for them.

Mr. Patton led in a prayer of thanksgiving, and then they opened their gifts to each other. Rod and Susie received ice skates which they tried out on a real pond the next day. Both agreed it was the best Christmas they had had so far.

Rod had not seen Pete for several days before he left town, and he wondered if his friend would be as friendly after their earlier tense conversation. When, after Christmas, Pete finally came over to borrow a wrench with which to work on his car, he made an effort to be unusually friendly, as if to cover up for his sharp words to Rod earlier.

"Hey, Rod, my church is sponsoring a football team for inner city kids, and I'm helping to coach. Would you like to come along this Saturday?"

"Yeah, it sounds interesting. How long have you been doing this?"

"Just a couple of months."

"You never mentioned it before," Rod said.

"It's no big thing." Pete shrugged.

"Yeah, I'd really like to go with you," Rod said.

On Saturday morning they were on the practice football field of a predominantly black high school in Watts. All of the kids were from the area. Rod had never been in that kind of situation before, and he was a little uncomfortable. Neither he nor Pete had considered that his heavy drawl would stand out so much, but the kids with whom they were working were young and they just laughed because he talked "funny."

They practiced for about an hour and then they scrimmaged. Rod and Pete acted as coaches for the opposing teams. Most of the boys were about twelve years old, and Pete had been teaching them well. They knew what they were doing, but they were anxious to accept Rod's guidance. Pete was really good with them, though Rod would never have expected him to be so patient. The boys obviously liked Pete and respected his football sense.

After an hour of hard-hitting playing, the boys claimed they were hungry enough to eat a horse. About that time two girls about Rod's age showed up with boxes of sandwiches, drinks, potato chips and cookies.

"Sandy Larson and Connie Hovis, meet Rod Patton." Pete introduced them. "The girls are from our church and they bring us food every week. We're always very nice to them. Right, fellows?"

Twenty greedy boys agreed loudly as they dug unceremoniously into the sandwich box.

"They're great kids," Pete said, as he and Rod ate at the end of the table and watched as the young football players ate ravenously. "This is the best meal some of them get all week."

"You're got to be kidding!" Rod exclaimed, surprised.

Pete shook his head. "No, most of them have terrible home lives—broken homes, homes where their parents beat them, homes where their father has raped their stepsister, homes where there is never enough to eat, homes where rats are a danger to them. Man, I never realized people lived the way some of these kids do. It's really been an eye-opener. Wow—the stories they tell."

"What do you say when they tell you these stories?" Rod asked.

"Mostly, I just listen and sympathize I guess. It seems to help them just to talk about it. I think what they need most is a friend, and that's what I try to be," Pete said.

Rod hesitated a moment, then asked, "Pete, do you

ever talk to them about your Church or about Christ?"

"No, I don't," Pete answered shortly.

"Do you think there's a chance that Christ might be the answer for them?" Rod asked.

Pete's facial muscles had grown tight. He spoke impatiently, "Well, they know this whole football thing is sponsored by the church and that I'm Catholic."

Rod gave up. Somehow he could not make Pete understand how he felt. All those boys with messed-up lives really looked up to Pete. They liked him and respected him. What a great opportunity to share Christ with them, and they really needed to know that God loved them. If they knew how to trust Christ every day, they could have some stability in the midst of the complete instability of their lives.

Rod had never been around people like these much, but in three hours with these kids he saw them as individuals. They hurt and had problems and needed love like everyone else, and he wanted to help them. He wanted to share Christ with them, but he didn't know how. He wondered if they would listen to him anyway.

He became aware of the tension growing between Pete and him, and he wanted very much to say or do something to erase the situation. While he was trying to think of something, Pete burst out angrily, "Rod, you're always talking about Jesus and the church in a way I don't understand. You make me uncomfortable, because you always make me feel that I'm not doing or saying enough, or that you know something I don't. If you were working here with these kids every week, what would *you* say to them? What would you say when they talk about their homes?"

"Well, Pete, I can't seem to explain it very well when I'm with you, but I'll start at the beginning and try."

"Okay," Pete said, "but let's get comfortable." He walked over and sat down under a tree. Rod joined him and began digging gently at the ground with his left heel as he concentrated on what he was about to say.

"Pete, the Bible says that God created man and breathed his own life into him. And then he gave man the freedom to choose—man could obey God or he could sin. And man chose to sin. He disobeyed God. When he did, man was separated from God. Every man from Adam on has had to make a decision too, whether to go with God or not.'

"Rod, can I ask you a question?"

"Sure, stop me any time."

"Do you really believe that Adam was a real man?" Pete wanted to know. He was earnest, but he looked extremely skeptical.

Rod looked Pete straight in the eyes as he replied, "Yes, I really do. I believe the Bible. There's a lot in it that I don't understand yet, but I believe that it's God's Word and that it's true."

"I don't think I could believe it that completely, but I see where you stand," Pete said. "Go on."

"Okay, so man is born separated from God, and that separation can eventually lead to eternal separation in hell. When men die, depending on the choices they individually make, they go either into the eternal presence of God or they will be forever separated from God."

"Or they go to purgatory for a while," Pete threw in knowingly.

"Pete, if you read the New Testament, you won't be able to find anything in it about purgatory." As Pete started to interrupt, Rod said huriedly, "But let's talk about that later. So man is separated on earth from fellowship with God. His number one problem is how to get back to God, how to bridge that separation."

Pete seemed to be listening carefully, and he nodded his head slightly.

"The Bible says," Rod went on, "that men have always come to God by faith. They always bridged the separation by realizing that they needed God in their lives and by believing in him in faith."

"But they had to keep the Ten Commandments," Pete said. "God said so."

"I was reading something about this the other day, Pete. The Ten Commandments were the basic law that God gave people to live by. They're also the most complete revelation of God's character that people had received up to that time. The purpose of the Law was to help people know how to live together and to regain their fellowship with God. You see, God really wanted people to know how to live right and how to worship him. But you know what they did instead? They said, 'Okay, we'll *do* everything the Lord has told us to do, right down to the very letter of the Law.' "

Rod paused for breath, warming up to his subject.

"Go on," Pete commanded briefly.

"Well, they tried to keep the Law—they even added to it, trying to explain it for the people. By Jesus' time, the Pharisees had made such a detailed system of it that it was impossible to keep it fully. That's why Jesus called the Pharisees hypocrites and blind men. Their whole lives were centered around trying to keep the Law and their own traditions, but they were completely blind to the true meaning of the Law that God had given them.

"That's kind of interesting," Pete said casually. "Where did you learn all that stuff?"

In spite of himself, a tinge of amazement had crept into his voice, but Rod was so intent on what he was going to say next that he failed to hear Pete. He was experiencing an inner excitement he had never known before, as well as a growing confidence in his ability to explain something of his own faith to his friend.

"See," he went on, "that's why they didn't accept

Jesus when he came. Jesus was the more complete revelation of God, but since they hadn't understood the
first revelation, how could they understand Jesus? The
Law didn't work, so God sent Jesus to bridge forever
the separation between God and man.

"Jesus died for our sins, so that when we believe in
him, our fellowship with God is restored. All our sins
are forgiven, and we are at peace with God. And not
only is the separation bridged, but God gives us his
Holy Spirit to live within us. And then we have a whole
other dimension of life. When we realize we can't save
ourselves and we can't do anything *for* God to make
ourselves acceptable, then we give up and look to God
for mercy. We stop trying to prove ourselves to God,
and we just accept what God has already done for us.
That's what grace means. And we invite Jesus Christ to
come into our lives and to be our Lord. That's the only
way we can be saved. It's the only way to bridge the
separation."

Pete was silent, obviously thinking. At last he said
without looking up, "I don't think I've ever done that.
In fact, I don't think I've ever heard of that before."

"But you can do it, Pete. God loves you and he wants
you to."

"Does that mean," Pete asked, seriously, "that going
to church and taking the sacraments doesn't help to
save you?"

"That's what it means. Your salvation isn't depend-
ent on anything you can do except to believe."

"That's not what my Church teaches," Pete said. He
was really serious now.

"Don't take my word for it, Pete. I'll give you a New
Testament, and you can read it for yourself."

Suddenly Pete laughed, breaking the tension that
had built up. "Wow, man, you've really been studying
up lately, haven't you? You sound like some preacher

or something. Or maybe a high-pressure salesman." He was beginning to sound like his usual self and a little condescending.

Rod's answering voice was as casual but serious. "Pete, I don't want to pressure you, but you asked me. That's what I would tell those little kids we've just been playing football with. When you invite Jesus into your life, he really comes in. And then you have the Spirit of God himself living in you. You have something real to offer those kids—not just a pat on the back occasionally."

Pete stood up, dug his hands into his pockets. "Rod, you're too much." He shook his head and laughed uncomfortably as if it was too much for him.

But Rod wouldn't give up yet. "You know something really wild, Pete?" he said in a low, firm voice as he climbed to his feet. "You're probably the only person in the world those kids would listen to right now talk to them about Jesus." He touched Pete lightly on the shoulder.

Pete stood very still, staring at Rod. Finally, his eyes turned cold and his face hardened, and he said, "I can't do that." He turned and walked off toward the practice field where two of the boys were playing catch. They included him immediately and made it a threesome.

4

ROD WAS ATTENDING BEVERLY HILLS HIGH AND DOING
well, even though the classes were more difficult than
those in his previous Texas school. The courses he enjoyed most were chemistry, American literature and
history, and he was making A's in all three. Richard
was in his chemistry class, and they worked together as
lab partners. They also studied together quite often.
One weekend they locked themselves in Rod's room to
cram for a Monday morning exam. They also taped a
sign on the door for Susie, who had no tests coming up
and wanted them to play Monopoly with her. The sign
read: "To whom it may concern, and especially to
Susie Patton: If you knock on this door one more time
tonight, you will be thrown into the swimming pool at
some inopportune time not of your own choosing. Let
this be a warning. Signed, The Mad Chemists."

Susie, who couldn't stand that kind of temptation for
an entire evening, restrained herself approximately one
hour before knocking and leaving the Monopoly set at
the door as she disappeared down the hall. Rod opened
the door, brought the Monopoly game inside and
stopped studying long enough to plot with Richard how

48

they would get her. In the midst of their discussion Richard brought up another subject.

"Rod, this may seem like kind of a strange time to ask you this, but I just remembered. Ann and I agreed the other day that we would like you and Susie to be our guests at the temple in two weeks for our Passover *seder*. We decided that since you were learning all about Buddhism from Pat and about Catholicism from Pete and running into all these crazy California cults, you should learn about Judaism from us. And we figure the *seder* is a good place to start."

"It's funny you mention that. I was thinking about it the other day. Seems like California itself is an education in religions of the world, and I was realizing I don't know anything about your religion. I'd really like to go."

"Susie probably will, too. She's always game to try something new," Richard said.

"It didn't take you long to figure out my little sister," Rod teased.

Richard grinned. "But you gotta admit she's cute," he said.

"Yeah, I guess so. You two seem to get along pretty well," Rod commented.

"I like her, I admit it." Richard smiled, and they returned to their plans of revenge on little sisters who do not heed personalized warning signs.

Richard was spending the night with Rod, so they could study late and start again immediately the next morning. Before they went to bed, they set their alarm for five A.M. When the alarm went off, they couldn't remember why they had set it so early. Confused, they stared at each other and the clock until Rod suddenly remembered.

They opened their door and tiptoed down the hall. Fortunately Susie had not locked her bedroom door, and they tiptoed in. They took places on each side of her bed; then they made a grab for her, wrapping her blanket around her.

Susie awoke with a start and began screaming. Her playful mood of the night before had vanished. She didn't know what was going on or why, and there was nothing funny to her about being awakened like that. She no longer remembered their threat of the night before. So she screamed madly all the way to the pool and into the air where they tossed her, and stopped only as she sank beneath the surface of the water. By this time Mr. and Mrs. Patton had come running out the back door.

"What on earth is going on, Rod?" Mr. Patton said angrily.

"Sorry, Dad. We didn't mean to wake you. We were just paying a little visit on Susie," he said.

"Rod, that's one of our best blankets," Mrs. Patton cried.

By this time Susie was rising out of the shallow end of the pool with the blanket draped around her like a mummy in a horror movie. She was really angry. She was also crying.

"Rod, I hate you," she screamed. She clenched her teeth, climbed out and stomped into the house with tears rolling down her already wet cheeks.

"Rod, you boys go on back to your room," Mrs. Patton said without smiling, "and we'll talk about this at a more decent hour today."

With that everyone returned to their rooms, and Rod and Richard carefully locked their door.

"Your folks weren't too happy," Richard said.

"Yeah, I guess it was kind of dumb." Rod scrubbed his hands through his hair. "You ever notice how the neatest ideas don't always work out the way you plan them?"

"Yeah, lots of times," Richard agreed as he climbed into bed. In a few minutes they both were asleep again.

Rod and Richard got off with a short, stern lecture on how April was not the month of the year to throw someone in the swimming pool at five o'clock in the morning. They both apologized to Susie and to Mr. and Mrs. Patton, and everyone returned to good terms.

Richard was right. After Susie recovered from her shock and anger over her early morning involuntary dip in the pool, she loved the idea of the Passover *seder*. Mr. and Mrs. Patton were a little reluctant at first because they had never heard of a *seder*, but when Richard explained to them briefly what it was, they agreed.

For the *seder* banquet the girls wore long peasant dresses, and the boys wore suits. It was the first time Rod or Susie had been inside a Jewish temple, and the surroundings were strange to them. In a large banquet hall the tables were lined up to seat about five hundred people, with the head table up on a stage. Richard's party was seated with his parents at a table very near the stage. Rod and Susie greeted Richard and Ann's parents and met their grandmother for the first time. A full orchestra was playing mood music in the background.

At each place beside the plate was a cup of wine and a printed booklet. Susie looked around and leaned over to Richard. "What's that?" she asked, indicating a dish in the center of the table.

"That's the *charoset*. It's a mixture of apples and nuts. It's really good. They'll explain during the *seder* what it means," Richard explained.

When almost every seat in the room was filled, a man whom Richard identified as the rabbi stood up at the head table and held up a cup of wine. Everyone stood and held up the wine cup beside his plate. The rabbi spoke a blessing first.

"Blessed art Thou, O Lord our God, Ruler of the world, Creator of the fruit of the grapevine."

Everyone responded by reading a blessing from the booklet called the *Haggadah*. Rod and Susie read along with them.

Blessed art Thou, O Lord our God, Ruler of the world, Who chose us out of all the people and selected us over all of the nations, and made us holy through His commandments. Lovingly, O Lord our God, Thou hast given us happy holidays and joyous festivals, this feast of Passover, anniversary of our freedom, a holy assembly, honoring our outgoing from Egypt; for Thou hast chosen us and made us holier than other peoples; and Thy holy festivals did Thou give us lovingly and kindly with happiness and joy. Blessed art Thou, O Lord, Who made the Sabbath, the people of Israel, and the festivals holy.

Everyone then drank from their wine cup.

Then the rabbi offered a blessing on the produce of the ground. "Blessed art Thou, O Lord our God, Ruler of the world, Creator of the produce of the earth." He explained the elements on the table: "As the wine is red in color and represents the blood of the Passover lamb, so also do the greens represent the hyssop which was used to place the blood of the Passover lamb upon the doorposts and the lintel. The salt water represents the tears shed in Egypt and the Red Sea, both of which are salty."

The rabbi then told the story of the exodus of the Hebrew people from Egypt. Rod and Susie followed every part of the ceremony in the *Haggadah*.

A plate on the table contained the shankbone of a lamb. The rabbi pointed to it when he got to the part of the ceremony which talked about the Passover lamb. "The Passover lamb which our forefathers ate in Temple times—for what reason? Because the Holy One, blessed be He, spared the houses of our ancestors in Egypt, as it is said: Ye shall declare, This is the Passover offering unto the Lord Who passed over the houses of the children of Israel when He struck Egypt and spared our houses."

The people bowed in worship.

After that the rabbi pointed to the *matzo,* which looked like large, thin unsalted crackers with stripes on them. "This *matzo* which we eat, what is the reason for it? It is because there was not enough time for our father's dough to rise, when the King of all Kings appeared when the Holy and Blessed One redeemed them. As the Scriptures say, 'and they baked the dough, which they had brought out of Egypt, into *matzo* cakes; for it had not risen, because they had been driven out of Egypt and could not tarry nor prepare food.' "

When the rabbi finished, each person ate a piece of *matzo.* Then the rabbi pointed to the *maror,* or bitter herb, on their plate. He said the *maror,* which was horseradish, represented the embittered lives of their forefathers in Egypt as their life was made bitter with hard labor. Everyone ate some of the horseradish on a piece of matzo, as the rabbi said, "The bitter herb speaks of the sorrow, the persecutions and the suffering of our people under the hand of Pharaoh; and as horseradish brings tears to the eyes, so also did the great affliction of our people bring tears to their eyes."

Susie got too much horseradish and had to have water administered quickly by Richard. He promised her that he had done the same thing at his first *seder.*

Then they ate the *charoset* on a piece of matzo while the rabbi told how the dish was a symbol of the mortar, representing the clay bricks, which were made by the Hebrews while they were in Egypt. Here the rabbi announced they would stop to eat dinner and would continue the services later.

Rod thought the meal was great. They had baked

chicken, green beans with mushrooms and almonds, and a baked potato. But the part Susie said she liked best was the *charoset*. The others at the table agreed with her. They all kept eating it right along with their dinner.

When the rabbi stood again and began the conclusion of the Passover ceremony, he said, "You will note that one place setting and one cup of wine has not been touched throughout the meal. This is the traditional place for Elijah. At this point in the service we open the door to see if the prophet Elijah will come."

A man got up and walked over to the side door of the auditorium. He opened the door and looked out, then closed the door and returned to his seat.

The rabbi continued, "You will also note that some items on the *seder* plate have not been touched. One is the roasted egg and the other is the shankbone of a lamb. The roasted egg speaks of sacrifice which can no longer be made because the Temple was destroyed. The shankbone of the lamb is untouched because lambs can no longer be sacrificed."

The people followed in the *Haggadah* what the rabbi was saying. "The *seder* of Passover is now complete. Just as we were privileged to celebrate it this year, so may we be privileged to do in the future," the rabbi concluded.

On the way home Rod and the others stopped at Bob's Big Boy to get soft drinks and to rap about the *seder*.

"That was really different from anything I've ever seen before. It's interesting, too," Rod said.

"Yes, I thought so, too. Thanks for inviting us, y'all," Susie agreed.

"Did you understand everything pretty well?" Richard wanted to know.

"Pretty well, I think, but it makes me want to study it some more," said Rod.

"I've got some books you can read if you want to," Richard offered.

Ann made a face. "Oh, those books aren't very good," she said. "I read my horoscope every morning, and it has more answers than they do."

"Well," Richard answered his sister, "let's let Rod read them and come to his own conclusions."

"That's great," said Rod. "Richard, I hope this won't offend you, but in a way I learned more about my own faith tonight."

"Oh? How exactly?"

"Well, do you know much about Jesus?"

"A little. I read some of the New Testament in school once, and I've read other things occasionally."

"Well, as Christians, we believe that Jesus *is* the Passover lamb and that all sacrifices before him were symbolic of God's promised Lamb to come. Like when they put the lamb's blood on the doorpost so the death angel would pass over and leave them safe. We believe Jesus died—shed his blood—for our sins so that we could live forever spiritually and never have to experience eternal death. We believe that he was the final sacrifice, and the New Testament says that's why sacrifice is no longer necessary," Rod explained.

"That's interesting," Richard said, thoughtfully.

Rod went on. "Also, it was at Passover *seder* that Jesus instituted the Lord's Supper with his disciples. He said that the unleavened bread represented his body which was broken for us and that the wine represents his blood which he shed on the cross for us. You see, for the Christian it all ties together."

For a moment Rod was silent. Then he asked, "Richard, what do you think of Jesus? I mean, have you ever thought that he really could be the Jewish Messiah?"

"No," Richard answered slowly, still thoughtful. "I guess I never seriously considered that possibility.

Jewish kids are taught in their homes that Jesus was a great teacher but that he could not possibly have been the Messiah."

Rod nodded, and said, "But Jesus didn't claim to be a great teacher. He claimed to be God, to be the Son of God in such a way that he was equal with God. If he claimed to be God and he wasn't, he'd be a liar. And if he based all his great teachings on a lie, he couldn't have been a very great teacher."

"I guess that is logical, isn't it? I never thought of that, but then I don't sit around thinking about Jesus very often," Richard said and grinned.

"Hey, let me suggest something," Rod said.

"Listen, you crazy Baptist, you've got something up your sleeve and I'm not interested in being converted." Richard laughed good-naturedly.

Rod laughed too. "Okay, okay, but just let me ask you this one thing. Do you really believe in God?"

Richard considered the question a moment. "Yeah, I think so," he answered, finally.

"Do you pray?"

"Sometimes, but nothing ever happens."

"Would you be willing to try an experiment?" Rod was trying hard to keep his tone of voice casual.

"Hmm. I might."

"Would you pray—say by yourself tonight—that if Jesus could possibly be God's true Messiah, that God would prove it to you?"

"Oh, I don't know about that," Richard said, looking doubtful about the entire thing.

"Why? What's the harm? If Jesus *is* the Passover Lamb and he can give you new life and a personal relationship with God so that your prayers will be answered, you want to know, right? I mean, if this is the ultimate truth, you don't want to miss out, right?" Rod asked.

Richard sat there with a slight grin on his face. "That's a pretty good pitch, I gotta admit," he said.

"Okay, it's a deal then?"

"Well, I'll have to think about it."

"That's fair enough. And I'll be praying that God will reveal himself to you and show you who Jesus really is."

Suddenly Richard leaned forward across the table. "Hey, I'll tell you what I *will* do."

"What?"

"I'd be willing to read some books on Jesus if you'll read these books on Judaism. Then we can discuss them," Richard said.

"Now that's a deal," Rod agreed.

It was after midnight when they got home. Rod got into his pajamas and into bed to read for a few minutes. There was a knock at the door.

"Come in," he said.

It was Susie, and she was also ready for bed. She ran across the room and jumped onto the middle of his bed, almost knocking him off onto the floor.

"What are you doing—" he shouted.

"You were fantastic!" she said with awe in her voice.

Her brother looked genuinely surprised. "What? What are you talking about?"

"Talking with Richard. Rod, that was really great. How'd you know what to say?"

Rod's eyes were entirely serious as he answered. "I really don't know. I never know what to say in a situation like that, and I was terrified he'd get mad the way Pete always does when I try to talk with him. I couldn't believe it myself," he said wryly.

By now Susie too was serious as she asked, "Where'd you get the ideas for what you were saying?"

Rod shook his head. "I really don't know, but it's blowing my mind. That's the first time I was ever conscious of praying while I was talking. I asked God to show me how to talk to Richard about Jesus. Maybe this is how he does it."

They were silent a few moments, then Susie asked hesitantly, "Do you think Richard will pray like you suggested?"

"Yeah, but maybe not tonight. The whole idea seemed to be too much for him. But if he's really honest, and I believe he is, eventually he'll have to pray."

"What will happen then? I mean, what if he prays and nothing happens?" she asked.

"I don't know. To be honest, it kind of scares me too, but I have to believe that something will happen. I found a verse in the Bible the other day—here, let me show you." Rod reached for the Bible on his night table beside the bed. He flipped through the pages. "Here it is—Jeremiah 29:13. 'You will find me when you seek me, if you look for me in earnest.' Doesn't that sound as if God will show the truth to any man who really wants to know the truth?"

"Yeah, I guess so. I guess I just don't have very much faith. What do you think about Ann?"

"Well, she's really into astrology right now. But if something starts happening with Richard, she'll have to drop her horoscopes and start noticing."

"It'll be interesting to watch and see what happens, won't it?" Susie asked, intrigued.

"Yeah, but we have to do more than that."

"What?" Susie raised her eyebrows in query.

"Well, as Richard reads these books, we'll have to talk with him and tell him about our own Christian experiences. We also have to pray for him, and for Ann too."

"Okay," Susie answered. If her voice sounded a little uncertain, Rod did not notice.

They sat for a few minutes, thinking about the evening, about the *seder* and what it had started. Then Susie burst out, "Rod, I hate to admit this, but I felt kind of like Richard when he said he prayed and nothing happened. I've never said that before, but it's true."

"Do you pray very much?"

"No, but I know I should."

"Then why don't you?"

"I don't know. I guess partly because nothing happens and because there are other things I'd rather be doing."

"I have the same problem."

After a moment Susie looked at Rod with a new question in her face. "Rod, how come we've never talked like this before?"

"I don't know." Suddenly his eyes became excited. "Hey, I asked Richard to do an experiment tonight. Why don't we do one?"

"Like what?"

"Let's pray for him, together, right now."

"Well, I guess I can do that," Susie said doubtfully.

"Okay, come on," he said, and he got down on his knees.

"On our knees?" Susie sounded startled.

Rod looked up at her. "Why not?"

She got down beside him and folded her hands on the bed. "You start," she said.

Rod bent his head and, after a minute, said, "Father, thank you for letting us go to the *seder* tonight with Richard and Ann. And thank you for showing me what it means that Jesus is the Passover Lamb. I pray now that you'll show Richard what that means. God, I believe that if Richard wants to know you, you'll help him. And we pray that you'll get Ann interested, too. Lord, we also want to pray for Pete and for Pat. Help me to be kind to them instead of being critical and help me to be able to tell them about Jesus." He paused a moment, then went on. "Thank you for our home and our parents, and thank you for loving us. In Jesus' name. Amen." Rod finished and waited for Susie.

Hesitantly she began, "God, I never prayed with anyone like this before, and you'll have to help me say the right thing. Please help Richard to learn about Jesus. And help Ann too. And show me how I can help. Thank you for loving us. In Jesus' name. Amen." She finished and stayed very still.

"That wasn't so bad, was it?" Rod asked.

"No," she said, but she didn't look convinced. "I'm really tired, and I think I'll go to bed."

"Okay, see you tomorrow." They stood up, and Rod said gently, "Thanks for praying with me." Susie nodded and closed the door behind her.

Several days later Pete stopped by. He hadn't been around since the day they played football with the inner-city kids. It had been almost two weeks, and Rod knew that Pete was avoiding him. It surprised him that, after waiting so long, Pete walked in with no obvious reason for being there.

"Just thought I'd stop by and say·hello," he said casually.

"Great! How about something to drink?" Rod offered.

"Okay, if you've got some of Susie's great lemonade."

"If we don't, I'll round her up and see that she makes some," Rod said, as he headed for the kitchen.

"That's a deal, man," Pete said. He was being very cool and casual, but he wasn't himself. He seemed to have something on his mind that he wasn't yet coming right out with.

Susie promised to make a fresh pitcher of lemonade if Rod and Pete would play Monopoly with her for a while. Pete said he would hang around awhile, but he could not stay too long. They set up the game in the middle of Rod's bedroom floor and played for about an hour as they snacked on lemonade and Mrs. Patton's homemade oatmeal cookies. Pete tried to be his old self, but he did not seem completely comfortable. Finally, he announced that he would have to be going. Susie took the glasses and cookie plate back to the kitchen while the boys put the Monopoly materials back in the box. When she left the room, Pete closed the door to Rod's room.

"Rod," he said, "I really came by to talk with you and see if there's any chance we can still be friends."

"Well, sure we can, Pete. Is there any problem?"

"You know what the problem is." Pete sounded exasperated. "You're a religious fanatic. That's all you talk about, and you even try to spoil the one good thing I've tried to do with those kids by telling me that I'm not doing the right thing or that I'm not doing enough. And I've just had it."

Pete dug his hands deep into his pockets and slouched against the door. "I like you, and I've enjoyed all the times we've spent together, but I don't want to talk about religion all the time with my friends. And I don't want to be made to feel that I'm not good enough for my friends."

"Pete, I never tried to make you feel that way," Rod protested. He was astounded at Pete's accusations and genuinely worried at the strength of his anger.

"Well, you do. And I've thought about it, and I decided I don't need that. At least, not from my friends." Pete used the word "friends" very sarcastically.

"Pete—"

"Just let me finish." Rod closed his mouth and listened. Pete had a strange gleam in his eye. "I was thinking about it today, and I came up with a really good way for you to prove to me that you're not a fanatic and that you'd really like to be my friend."

"Okay. What is it?"

Pete's lip curled into a sneer. "It'll be a real test, Rod, if you're up to it." Rod frowned and waited for what was coming. "I went up on the Strip today and scored. I picked up a kilo of grass, and I thought maybe you'd like to join me in my backyard for a little party, just the two of us."

"Grass?" Rod couldn't believe it. "You want me to smoke grass with you?"

"Why not? Are you man enough? I want real men for my friends, not religious namby-pambies. How about it, Rod?" Pete no longer seemed uncomfortable. He had put out his bait and was waiting very deliberately for Rod's answer.

"Well, I didn't expect anything like that." Rod moved worriedly around the room.

"Well, what's the answer?"

After a long moment, Rod faced Pete steadily. "The answer is no," he said. "I want to be your friend but not if that's the way I have to prove it. When I first came here, I would probably have backed down if you had called me a fanatic and done just about anything to prove I wasn't and to make friends. But I'm just beginning to discover that my Christian faith is really exciting, and if that makes me a fanatic to you, then that's too bad. I like you, Pete, and I think this whole thing is stupid. I can't believe you would really call this a test of our friendship." Rod was angry and hurt.

Pete straightened up and shrugged. "Well, in that case, Rod, baby, I'm not the least bit interested in your friendship anymore. I wish you the best with the saints and the monks. As for me, I think there's a lot more to life than that, and I'm going to get high and enjoy life. I hope you don't die of boredom." Pete opened the bedroom door, walked out and slammed it behind him.

Rod sat down suddenly on his bed, stunned.

5

THE HOUSE WAS DEFINITELY QUIETER SINCE PETE DID not come around anymore. Rod missed Pete and he still had a hard time believing what had happened. Mr. and Mrs. Patton asked about Pete, and Rod just said that he wasn't very close anymore. He didn't want to tell his parents about the confrontation over marijuana. Secretly he kept hoping that Pete would call and everything would be back the way it was.

After almost a year in a California high school Rod knew that drugs were an everyday part of the teen-age culture in Los Angeles. But his parents were not so well-informed. When they talked about drugs, it was obvious they did not believe the situation could possibly be as bad as the news media said. Rod was not sure what would happen if his parents realized that Pete smoked grass occasionally. He did talk to Susie about what had taken place. She too was aware of the drug problem, for many of the girls she knew at school took some kind of narcotics. She was not surprised that Pete smoked grass, but she was very surprised that he gave Rod such an ultimatum.

"I guess the praying thing is what bothers me the

most," Rod said. "I don't understand a lot about praying, but I keep reading in the Bible where it says that you must believe you are going to receive what you pray for. I really believed that I would be able to talk to Pete better than I had before. Now I'll probably never be able to talk to him again, and I don't even know what I did wrong."

"Rod, maybe someday you *will* get to talk with him, though." Susie said, trying to console him. "You never know. Maybe Pete will respect you for what you did."

"I don't know." Rod sounded doubtful. "But it's really discouraging, especially since I don't understand it at all. I guess I'll just keep praying for him that he'll change his mind about me." He walked over to look out of the window.

"Well, Ann's coming over this afternoon," Susie said, trying to change the subject.

"Any special reason?"

"No, just to visit."

Ann brought with her several fashion and beauty magazines she had just picked up on the newsstand and also a horoscope publication. She and Susie flipped through them, reading an article on hair styling and one on "how to catch the right guy." They compared and discussed the fashion pages. Both girls liked to keep up with the latest styles but had difficulty getting their mothers to agree with their tastes.

"When you wear lashes, how do you get them on so straight?" Susie wanted to know.

"I use a toothpick to make sure I get them right next to my real lashes," Ann confessed.

"Will you show me how to do it sometime?"

"Sure."

"Mom doesn't like me to wear them, but I bought a pair and sometimes I practice putting them on. I just don't do it very well yet."

"Sure, I'll be glad to help. It's real easy once you get the hang of it," Ann said, encouragingly. She was still flipping pages in one of the magazines. One page caught her attention. "Hey, wanta hear your horoscope?"

"Why not?"

"What sign are you?"

"Scorpio."

"Okay, here you are. 'The Sun moves into your Twelfth House on the 24th. This will continue the emphasis of last week on psychological and emotional states of mind. You should study things of an occult or hidden nature while the Sun occupies this part of your horoscope. You may receive help from unexpected sources, and you should be careful to be sure that everyone you speak with understands what you mean and that there is no room for misinterpretation. Venus aspects later in the week indicate a harmonious atmosphere with a more relaxed pace.' "

"That's really confusing if you don't know anything about astrology," Susie said, adding, "and I don't."

"But it's really interesting to study it and start finding out all kinds of things about yourself," Ann said.

"Do you?" Susie asked. "Study it, I mean."

"Oh, a little."

"What's your sign?" Susie asked.

"I'm Virgo.'

"Let's hear yours."

"Okay. Here it is." Ann found her place and read: " 'The Full Moon this week is in your Seventh House. Marriage and love relations will be accented by this Moon and there may be some dramatic event centering around a relationship. A Mars trine with Uranus suggests unexpected financial activity with some positive changes. Don't be afraid to change things which you know must eventually be changed. Venus in your

First House forms two creative aspects which indicate that there will be the opportunity for you to develop a talent which you potentially have. Try and learn new things and remain open to change this week.' "

"Ann, do you really take all this horoscope stuff seriously?" Susie wanted to know.

Ann nodded. "Yeah, I think it's really true. They can tell you everything about yourself. You can know when to do things and when not to do them. It's fascinating."

Susie raised her eyebrows as if confused. "It just all sounds phony to me," she said.

"Oh no, it's very scientific," Ann protested. She sounded distressed. "Listen to this:

Man lives on the Earth; but he is active as well within the galaxy which not only envelops but pervades the whole solar system. Most living organisms on this Earth find their lives completely determined by solar energies and seasonal patterns; but man has the innate capacity to develop a mind (and through this mind, various vital responses) which can challenge the normal rhythm of solar energies. Symbolically speaking, he can reach a level of response at which he can feel, think and even partially act as a "galactic being" rather than as a "solar-system being."

Susie shrugged. "That's all beyond me," she responded without interest.

"Look, Sue," Ann leaned forward, "Doesn't it seem reasonable that if the planets and the moon can affect the tides and gravity and nature they can also affect human personality?" she asked.

"I don't know. See, I have to start with what I do know," Susie explained, "and I know that God exists and that his Bible is true. And I don't know of anything in the Bible that says we should go to astrology to find answers to life. In fact, as a Christian, I think I'm sup-

posed to go to the Bible for that kind of information."
Susie spoke, carefully choosing her words.

"But, Susie, you're trying to ignore something that's true. You can't do that. The facts are there—it's true," Ann said firmly.

Susie felt flustered because Ann was so sure of herself, and Susie didn't really know much about astrology. But she went on slowly. "Ann, I don't have all the answers, and I know it. The only thing I can think of is that just because something is true doesn't mean it's good. If there really is a Satan and I believe there is, then he has powers to do things which are true, but they aren't good."

"Really, Susie! Satan?"

"The Bible says he's real," Susie said, determinedly holding her point.

"Well, maybe the Bible's a little out of date too," Ann answered stiffly.

"I used to think that too, but lately Rod's gotten me to reading it more. I'm finding that it's pretty relevant. I feel kind of like what you said about your astrology book—it really applies to my life. When I do what it tells me, it works," Susie said.

For a moment neither girl spoke. Then Ann threw out casually, "I've been thinking about reading the Bible myself."

"What?" Susie thought that maybe she hadn't heard right.

"I glanced through one of those books Rod gave Richard to read," Ann admitted, "and it had some pretty interesting things in it. So I thought I might look into it. I'm open to anything, and I'm willing to admit astrology may not have all the answers." She added quickly. "But I'm not giving it up till someone proves to me it's all wrong or all stupid or something."

They made pecan cookies and read several other magazines, but Susie could hardly wait for Ann to leave so she could tell Rod what had happened. Finally, as Ann was leaving, Susie offered her a modern English translation of the New Testament. Ann took it and planted it between a couple of magazines so her mother wouldn't see it when she got home.

"She'd have a stroke if she knew I even had a New Testament, much less was reading it," she said.

"I promise not to tell," Susie said happily and winked at her.

She closed the door behind Ann and went straight toward Rod's room.

"Rod! Rod!" She called at the top of her lungs.

She flung open the door to Rod's room.

Her brother was working at his desk. He looked slightly irritated.

"You won't believe what I have to tell you," she said, ignoring his visual rebuke.

"All right, what?"

"Ann's going to start reading the New Testament." She glowed with the pleasure of breaking the news to him.

Rod's attention immediately changed from his chemistry textbook to Susie.

"You're kidding," he said. He stared at her.

"Nope." Susie sat down on the bed. She grinned at him.

"Wow! That's great!" he said. "How did that happen?"

"Well, she was telling me how great astrology was, and I was going crazy trying to think of what to say about horoscopes. Then all of a sudden she was telling me that the books you gave Richard were pretty interesting, and she might start reading the Bible her-

self. So just before she left, I gave her a modern translation of the New Testament to take with her. How about
that!" Susie said, pleased with herself.

"Wow! I just don't believe it."

"I didn't either." Her brother jumped up, took a
turn around the room, and slapped his hands together.
"Oh, wow, that is *really* something!"

"Rod," Susie asked in a different tone of voice,
"what do you believe about astrology? I mean, is
there any truth to it?"

"I honestly don't know," Rod answered, a serious
tone in his voice.

"Well, how can we find out? I think we need to
know if we're going to talk with Ann."

Rod walked over to the window and looked out.
After a moment he turned and said, "I know. Let's
get some of Dad's concordances and topical diction-
aries and look it up," Rod suggested. They went to
the den to the bookshelf and returned a few minutes
later loaded with thick books. They dumped these in
the middle of Rod's bed, and each of them got busy.
They were quiet for a long time while they were reading.

"Hey, listen to this, Susie," Rod exclaimed at last,
excitedly. "Read 1 Samuel 28, starting about verse 7.
A medium actually brought Samuel's spirit back so
Saul could talk to him. And it doesn't say it was impossible to do; it just says it wasn't good. Samuel said
he was being disturbed."

"That's not the same thing as astrology," Susie said.

"True, but spiritism is connected with astrology,
according to this book."

They continued reading, until Rod broke out again.
"Susie, listen to this section in Isaiah 47. 'Stand fast
now in your spells and in your many sorceries with
which you have labored from your youth; Perhaps

you will be able to profit, perhaps you may cause trembling. You are wearied with your many counsels, let now the astrologers, those who prophesy by the stars, those who predict by the new moons, stand up and save you from what will come upon you. . . . There is none to save you.' "

"Does that mean that you can actually do things with astrology, but it can't save you from hell?" Susie asked.

"Sounds like it. Or that it can't provide any real answers to life," Rod said.

Susie looked across at the desk. "Hey," she said, "let's write some of these things down." She got up to get a pencil from the desk.

"Okay, and here's another one. Write down Amos 5:4–8. Listen to part of it: 'For thus says the Lord to the house of Israel, Seek me that you may live. . . . He who made the Pleiades and Orion and changes deep darkness into morning, Who also darkens day into night, who calls for the waters of the sea and pours them out on the surface of the earth, The Lord is His name. It is He who flashes forth with destruction upon the strong, so that destruction comes upon the fortress.' "

Rod looked up from his reading. "That says God made all the stars and the stuff astrologers study, and we should worship God instead of the stuff he made. That's the real truth, Susie, and that's what we should tell Ann," he said.

"Rod, could we pray again?" Susie said timidly.

Her brother nodded. "Yeah. I think that's a great idea. You want to right now?"

"Yes."

They got on their knees again beside the bed with all the books and Bibles open in front of them. Rod began their prayer.

"Father, we're so excited about Ann we don't know what to do. I guess I didn't have enough faith, because I didn't expect anything to happen with her this soon. Thank you for giving her an interest in reading the Bible, and thank you for letting Susie talk to her. And thanks also for letting us find these verses about astrology in the Bible."

He paused a moment then went on, "Lord, I pray that you'll make Richard interested too. And, Lord, I pray that you'll straighten out whatever I did wrong with Pete. And, God, I also pray for Pat. Help her to find Jesus. Thank you for helping Susie and me to pray together this way, and thank you for answering our prayers. Thank you for loving us and for sending Jesus to die for us. I pray in his name. Amen."

Susie prayed more eagerly this time. "Heavenly Father, thank you so much for Ann. I still can't believe what happened with her today. Help her really to know the truth as she reads the New Testament. And, God, show me what to say to her when we talk about astrology again. Thank you for Rod and for our parents. In Jesus' name. Amen."

She sat quietly for a moment, and then her face lit up. "I can't wait to see what's going to happen next," she said.

"Me, too," Rod agreed.

Susie had started looking at some of the books again. "Hey, this book says the Tower of Babel was an observatory for idolatrous worship of the stars, and God showed his attitude toward such observatories by destroying it. Did you know that's what it was?"

"I never really thought about it," Rod said.

"It goes on to say that in Deuteronomy 18 the Mosaic law commanded astrologers to be put to death," Susie said.

They spent at least another hour buried in the Bible

and the concordance, and they made lots of notes. They could hardly wait for their next opportunity to go over with Ann the things they had found.

Rod's birthday was in May and Susie planned a surprise party around their pool. He was embarrassed when he arrived with Richard who was part of the plan and who helped to sneak him away from the house. He was always self-conscious with groups of people, especially when they centered their attention on him. Ann and Pat were there and several of Rod's friends from school. Susie had invited Pete also but she wasn't surprised when he didn't show up.

They brought out a huge cake and sang "Happy Birthday" while Rod just stood there, red to his ears. Then everyone broke up into little conversational groups while Ann and Susie grilled the hamburgers and hot dogs.

Steve Manderley, who was in Rod's lit class, wanted to know where Pete was.

"Didn't you guys used to spend a lot of time together? I thought you were pretty good friends," he said.

"Yeah,—well, we've been kind of going in different directions lately. You know, different interests," Rod said.

"No big misunderstanding or fight?" Steve pressed.

"What makes you think that?"

"Well, Pete's let the word out with a few people at school that you aren't the greatest friend in the world. He says you're a religious fanatic and that you really let him down when he needed you," Steve reported. His eyes, looking into Rod's, were noncommital.

Rod looked as though someone had thrown cold water in his face. He and Susie had discussed the situation, prayed about it, and made a pact not to talk to anyone else about it. It hadn't occurred to him that

Pete would talk freely about it and perhaps even color it to suit his own interests. Pete was the one who needed a few lessons in friendship.

Richard had been standing with them all this time listening to Steve's conversation. "Rod, you didn't tell me that you and Pete had a blowup," he said, surprised.

"It's a personal problem between Pete and me, and I didn't see any need to discuss it with anyone else," Rod said.

"Well, I just thought you ought to know he's not giving you the same courtesy," Steve said.

"That's too bad, but it doesn't mean I have to stoop to that level. Hey, are you guys ready for a hamburger?" Rod offered. He maneuvered them over to the grill where they got their meat and then to the picnic table for all the other food. Rod drifted away from them and sat down alone at the other end of the pool.

He decided he must really be naive since it had not even occurred to him that Pete would talk up their problem with the kids at school. He wondered what Pete had actually said about him. Had Pete just told his opinion of what took place or had he lied? And how many of the kids here at the party knew something?

"Hey, no fair. You're the birthday boy today, and you can't sit off by yourself like this." It was Pat. She had her plate in her hand, and she plopped down in the chaise lounge next to his chair.

"How are you, Pat?"

"Fine, and yourself?"

"Okay."

"You don't look it. You look like you're carrying the weight of the world on your shoulders," she said, teasing him.

"Nope. I was concentrating on something for a minute. How was your Nichiren Shoshu convention?"

"Really great! There were people there from all over. The parties were great, and we met lots of neat people. But it was really spiritual too."

"Oh? How?"

"Well, all the Buddhists are working together for *kosenrufu,* which is world peace. And the more people you have chanting together and tuning into the vital life force at the same time, the heavier it is. Wow! It was really fantastic! And how's Jesus these days?" she asked, tongue in cheek.

"He's great," Rod said, smiling at her.

"Getting to know a lot about him, huh?" she asked.

"Better than that." Rod smiled.

Pat looked a little surprised at the quiet assurance in his voice. "What do you mean?" she asked.

"Getting to know *him.*"

"Oh, yes," she said sarcastically, "He's still alive, isn't he?"

"That's right," Rod was still smiling.

"Rod, that's so ridiculous. Like that silly song the Baptist kids in my neighborhood used to sing, something about 'he walks with me and he talks with me.' Oh, boy!"

"It does sound corny that way, doesn't it? But it's true. And you know something else, Pat?"

"What?" She was not smiling, but watched Rod curiously.

"This Jesus, who's still very much alive and walking and talking with people, loves you."

"Oh, come on, Rod," she said, obviously irritated.

"It's true, Pat, and I never thought I'd ever be able to say that to you." Rod grinned wryly, but the assurance was still in his voice.

"Why?"

"Well, you emphasize being intellectual so much, and you've always intimidated me," Rod admitted, grinning. He was relaxed and not a bit uptight.

"How come you can do it now?"

"Because Jesus who is alive is changing me. I used to think the most important thing in talking with other people was to prove a point or to show them the truth of the Bible. Now I'm beginning to understand that the most important thing is to love 'em. You see," he said, glancing at her, "it's difficult for you to listen to what I say about the love of Jesus if I'm uptight about *your* religious beliefs."

Pat looked a little surprised. "That's for sure true. And I'm sure you're going to be much more pleasant to have around this way, but I'm still not interested in Jesus or in his loving me," she finished firmly.

"But that's okay, too. Because he loves you whether you're interested or not, and so do I. And I learned something else that makes me less uptight, Pat."

"What now?"

Rod laughed. "I learned that it isn't my responsibility to prove God or Jesus to you. God is capable of proving himself, if you want him to. My responsibility as a Christian is to share with you what Jesus is doing in my own life and to pray for you," he explained.

"Now, that really offends me," Pat said, anger in her face and voice.

"What?"

"Rod, I don't need you or anyone else praying for me."

"Even if I do it out of love and concern for you?"

"Not for *any* reason," she said, still furious.

"Pat, I'm sorry if that offends you, but I have to be honest and tell you that I pray for you every day."

"I think you're trying to turn the tables and intimidate me, but I'm not going to get uptight. I don't like it, but if you want to waste your time praying for me, that's your business. I should care!"

She laughed uncomfortably, and Rod changed the subject. "Hey, tell me about that new puppy you got the other day. You should have brought him to the party."

Pat talked about the puppy, but her face showed she was still thinking about the fact that Rod was praying for her. It obviously disturbed her. Gradually, describing her new dog, she began to seem relaxed and happy. But Rod knew that later she would have to search out in her mind what it really meant to her that a Christian cared enough about her to pray for her every single day.

6

"SUSIE, YOU'LL NEVER GUESS WHAT MR. CLARK IS doing," Rod said one day on the way home from church.

"Your Bible teacher?"

"Yeah."

"What's he doing that's so great?"

"Every Monday night he and his wife have a couple of Mormon preachers over to talk with them about Mormonism. Then the Clarks share with these guys what we believe about Christ. He says it's really great."

"Sounds interesting."

"They're learning a lot about Mormonism, and the Mormon guys are beginning to get interested in our understanding of the Holy Spirit."

"Wow!"

"Mr. Clark invited us to come over sometime if we want to. Janice went over last Monday night, and she said she really learned a lot. Wanta go sometime?"

"Sure. I'd love to."

Their church also sponsored rock concerts in its basement during the summer for young people on the Strip. The Christian teen-agers would canvass the

Strip on a Friday or Saturday night passing out free tickets to the concert. After an hour of music, Christian testimonies and a brief, "unpreachy" message by the pastor, they all had sandwiches and punch and talked about Jesus. Rod had been elected to serve on the young people's committee to organize this summer's concerts. And Susie had agreed to help make sandwiches every weekend.

Richard did not understand why Susie was willing to commit her weekends that way, but he dated her whenever he could. Occasionally he went to the concerts with her. They were different from anything he had been to before. He confided to Susie that he never let his parents know exactly where he was on those nights, for it bothered them enough that he was dating a Gentile girl. The fact that she was a strong Christian believer did not reassure them. They would really make a scene if they knew he was reading the New Testament and visiting a Baptist church. They had never emphasized Judaism in their home, and they had no strong religious beliefs of their own, but they had been extremely upset when a cousin "converted."

Richard would not admit to Rod or Susie whether or not he had prayed for God to show him the truth. But he questioned them for long periods, so they knew he was reading a lot in the New Testament now. He tried to keep it on an intellectual level. After one Friday night of rock concerts the three of them stopped for coffee on the way home.

"How's your reading coming?" Rod asked.

"Okay. I still have questions though," Richard said.

"Like what?" Susie wanted to know.

"All this stuff about law and grace is confusing to me," Richard said.

"What does Judaism say about the Law, Richard?" Rod asked.

"Well, first you have to realize that there are three divisions of Judaism—Orthodox, Reform and Conservative. Orthodox believes in a rigid adherence to the Law and also to a lot of rabbinic teachings. Reform Judaism is mostly humanism. It's very liberal and doesn't hold to the Law. Conservative Judaism is sort of in the middle between the two."

"That's interesting. Sometimes I tend to think that only Christianity has divisions or denominations in its faith," Rod said. "Do most Jews believe that God expects them to keep the Law?"

"I suppose so," Richard answered.

"Do you try to keep the Law?"

"I guess I do. I keep the Law the best I can, and I try to do more good than bad."

"What Paul says in the New Testament about law and grace is that it is impossible for man to keep the Law. He says if you want to get right with God through the Law you must keep every single law and you can never break one."

"Uhmm, and what about grace?" Richard asked.

"God in his love and mercy provided another way; he sent Jesus. Jesus kept the Law completely so that he could be the sacrifice for us—the Passover Lamb."

"The *seder?*"

"Right."

"Grace is God's, uh, free and unmerited gift. All I have to do is take it. I can't do anything to deserve it; I can only accept it," Rod explained.

"Yeah, but how does that really work," Richard asked, "like in *your* life?"

"Well, several years ago I accepted Jesus as my Savior. I accepted, uh, what he did for me when he died. Now I am experiencing what it is to have his Spirit in me, guiding my life. He not only died for me; he also lives for me," Rod said.

"Well, I'm not ready for anything like that yet." Richard slid his hands into his pockets. "But it's interesting."

"Richard, what do the Jews believe about the Messiah if they don't accept Jesus? I always wondered how Isaiah 53 could refer to anyone other than to Jesus. Do you know the chapter I mean?"

"Yeah, I do." Richard nodded. "Many Jews are still waiting for the Messiah, but others believe those prophecies which everyone relates to the Messiah really mean Israel as a nation. Most Jews would probably say that Isaiah 53 refers to Israel," he said.

Richard was an interesting paradox. At one moment he would ask a serious question as though his life depended on the answer. The next he would completely rebuff the entire Bible. Sometimes he seemed intensely interested; at other times the whole thing seemed ridiculous to him. Rod and Susie answered his questions the best they could, and they tried not to pressure him. He wanted to study and to have discussions, but he did not want to be pushed.

Next day it was raining when Rod woke up. He sat at his bedroom window watching the rain on the swimming pool. Later, he found Susie on the floor in the den, working a jigsaw puzzle.

"Rod, come help me," she urged.

"In a minute," he said offhandedly.

"Are you depressed?"

"I don't know. I never did like rain. I guess I'm just bored," he said.

"Come work the puzzle with me."

"No, that's not what I want to do."

"Anything I can do?"

"No." He walked across the room to stare out the window.

The phone in the kitchen rang, and he heard his

mother answer it. Then she called casually down the hall, "Rod, it's for you. It's Pete."

Rod and Susie reacted as if they had been hit by lightning. Rod was off and halfway down the hall in a flash. Susie followed quickly.

"Hello. I'm glad to hear from you, Pete—Hey, what's wrong?—Pete, Tell me what's wrong." He was listening. Susie was staring at him.

"Oh, wow, that's horrible. Pete, come on over here and let's talk. Of course, I don't mind. I want you to. Okay, I'll see you in a minute. Bye." Rod hung up the phone very slowly.

"What on earth?" Susie asked.

"Wow! Remember the day I went with Pete to play football with these kids he's working with?"

"Yes."

"One of the twelve-year-old kids killed himself last night!"

"Oh, no! How terrible!"

"Pete's really upset. He was crying on the phone."

"Did he just find out?"

"Yeah, the priest called earlier this morning," Rod said.

"You know, I remember Pete saying one time that none of his close relatives or friends had ever died. And he didn't know how he would react to the death of someone he knew. I guess this is the first time," Susie said sadly.

"He sounded awful on the phone," Rod said.

"But, Rod, it's a good sign that he's coming to you," she said.

Pete was there in about five minutes. He wasn't crying now, but he almost seemed to be in shock. He and Rod sat down in Rod's room. Susie had taken her puzzle to her room to let them be alone.

"Pete, what happened?" Rod asked.

"I really don't know, Rod. I just wanted to talk with you." He stopped and there was a long pause. Rod sat quietly and waited. After a few seconds Pete's lip began to tremble.

"Rod, I'm sorry. I've done everything wrong. I've been a lousy friend to you, and I want to apologize." He was staring out the window and wouldn't look at Rod.

"It's okay, Pete. Now, what can I do to help you?"

"I thought I was really helping those kids. They were going to have better lives because I had taught them to play a good, honest game of football. I was teaching them skills and fair play, and I figured that was really great. But, man, it wasn't enough for Charlie."

"You couldn't help what happened, Pete," Rod said.

"But maybe I *could* have." Pete slumped over, his face in his hands.

"What do you mean?"

"Rod—" Pete's voice cracked. "Charlie came to me last week and asked for help. His mother is a heroin addict, and she didn't care anything about Charlie. He was just another mouth to feed, and she needed the money to support her habit. She told him that day that she didn't want him around anymore. He didn't know what to do or where to go. He wanted help, and I didn't have any." Pete's voice broke and he had to wait a moment before going on. "I really didn't know what to say to him. So I just told him not to worry, that everything would be okay. He even played football that day, but he wasn't concentrating on the game."

Rod just sat and listened. He didn't know what to say.

Pete continued. "Rod, nobody loved that kid, least of all me. And I keep remembering what you said about them needing to know that God loved them. Charlie needed to know that. And all I could tell him about was football." Pete's hands clinched and un-clinched. "When they found his body, they figured he hadn't eaten in about four days and had been out on the streets all during that time. Last night he broke into his mother's house and got her gun out from under her bed and shot himself in the head."

Rod searched for words to help. "Pete, you tried to help. You just didn't know how," he said, trying to sympathize.

Pete shook his head. "That's just it. Trying wasn't good enough, and what I'm doing for myself isn't good enough, either."

"What do you mean?" Rod looked up, surprised.

"I've been having a great time like I told you, get-ting high and just enjoying life," Pete explained. "And I'm miserable. I loused up things with you—it wasn't your fault I treated you the way I did. And I loused things up for Charlie, and even for me. And now I don't know what to do. You're the only person I could think of to talk to. Rod, I just despise myself." He put his hands over his face as great sobs shook his whole body.

After a moment Rod said, "Pete, you need to know the same thing that Charlie needed—that God loves you. No matter what, Pete, God loves you."

Pete pulled his handkerchief out of his pocket, blew his nose and said, "This is gonna sound corny, but I want to know what life is all about, and you seem to have a better idea than I do. I'm not interested in football and smoking grass and being Mr. Cool any-more. That's not where it's at." He looked up. "Rod, help me. Tell me what I should do." He was com-pletely defeated; he had given up.

Slowly, carefully choosing his words, Rod began to speak. "Pete, as far as I'm concerned, the only real purpose in life is in Jesus. He loves you and he died for you. He wants to come to you, to take over your life. But you'll have to let him. He can make you happy that way. And he can give you purpose for living," Rod said.

"Are you talking about something other than believing in the Church and in the sacraments?"

"Yes, I am. You see, Jesus was resurrected. That means he's alive now. So God gives his Spirit to those people who invite Christ to take over their lives. I don't know how to say it right, but it's not just words or something the Bible says. It's real. Jesus will really change your life."

Pete nodded. "I need that, but are you talking about what I do every day when I ask Jesus to come into my life?"

"No, because this is a once-for-all. Once Jesus comes within you, he never leaves."

"Not even when you sin?" Pete asked incredulously.

"Never. The Bible promises you that. Let me see if I can explain. If Jesus left every time you sinned, that would mean your salvation depended upon you and how you live."

"Yeah, I guess that's right," Pete said slowly.

"But, Pete, the Bible says your salvation depends only on Jesus. He is the only one who can save you. You have to realize that you can't save yourself."

"I'm sure not doing a very good job, am I?" Pete admitted dismally.

"No, you aren't. But God can do it for you. Pete, I've never done this with anyone before, but would you like to pray right now and give your life completely to Christ?"

Pete sat very still. He seemed pale and empty. Finally, he shrugged his shoulders. "I sure don't have anything to lose," he said. "Yeah, I'd like to, Rod."

"Will you read a couple of Bible verses first?"

"Okay," Pete said.

Rod picked up his Bible, flipped through it and found John 1:12. He handed the Bible to Pete with his finger on the verse. "Here, read it out loud for both of us," he said.

" 'But as many as received him,' " Pete read, " 'to them he gave the right to become children of God, even to those who believe in his name.' "

"Now look at this one," Rod said, as he found Acts 16:30 and 31.

" 'And after he brought them out, he said, "Sirs, what must I do to be saved?" And they said, "Believe in the Lord Jesus, and you shall be saved, you and your household." ' "

"And one more," Rod said, turning to 1 John 5:11–13.

" 'And the witness is this, that God has given us eternal life, and this life is in His Son. He who has the Son has the life; he who does not have the Son of God does not have the life. These things I have written to you who believe in the name of the Son of God, in order that you may know that you have eternal life.' "

"Come on, Pete, and let's pray," Rod said. He got down on his knees beside the bed.

Pete followed his lead. "What should I do?" he asked.

"Well, I never did this before either with anyone except Susie, but I'll pray first and then you pray. Okay?"

"What'll I pray?" Pete wanted to know.

"Just tell God whatever you feel right now. Tell

him you want him to come in and take over your life,"
Rod suggested.

"I never prayed that way before," Pete said doubtfully.

"It's not so hard. Just talk as if you're talking to me
right now."

"I'll try."

They knelt, and for a moment both were quiet.
"Father," Rod prayed, at last. "I thank you that you
love us, and that you bring us to the point where we
give up and let you have our lives. God, I thank you
for the way you are helping Pete right now. I thank
you for allowing me to be his friend." He hesitated,
then went on. "And I thank you for all that you have
promised to do in Pete's life as he trusts you. In Jesus'
name, Amen."

The room was again quiet for a few moments while
Pete tried to control himself. He wiped at his eyes
with his shirt sleeve. Rod prayed silently for him as he
waited.

"God—I thought all my life I knew you—but—
well, Rod is telling me that there is more to you than
the Church and all the sacraments I've been taught.
And I see something—in Rod's life that I never had.
I want it, God. I'm so sorry about Charlie—" Pete
started to cry again. "I wanted to help him, I really
did—but I didn't know how. I'm a failure at everything and I need your help. Jesus, please come into my
life for real and—and—show me what all this means.
I give up doing my own thing—I've only made myself
—and everyone else—miserable. God, you just do
what you can with my life. Amen."

Pete remained kneeling and slumped over the bed,
sobbing for some time. Rod turned around and sat
quietly on the floor beside him. Finally Pete was calm.

He turned around and sat beside Rod. Neither one said a thing for a long time.

Finally Pete said, "Rod, I feel so relieved. I feel like a whole big weight has been lifted off me."

"It has, Pete. Remember when Jesus said, 'Come to me, all of you who are tired from carrying your heavy loads, and I will give you rest'?" Rod asked.

"Yeah. Now I know what it means. Thanks, Rod," Pete said.

"You're really my brother in Christ now," Rod said, and they shook hands, smiling.

"It's great, so really great," Pete said.

"Susie's down the hall, and she's probably praying for you. Would you like to go tell her what you just did?"

"Yeah. Go with me?" Pete asked.

"I wouldn't miss it."

Susie hugged Pete and cried, she was so happy.

Rod and Susie had never had an experience like this before. They had always believed that people came to Christ, but they had just never seen it happen the way they saw it with Pete. Nor had they ever been part of a person's coming to Christ. A week later they were sitting in Rod's room, talking about it again.

"Pete's doing so great," Susie said. "He's really like a different person."

"You know who else noticed it?" Rod asked her.

"Who?"

"Pat!"

"Really? What did she say?"

"She said something must have happened to him because he was really different. She couldn't believe it when I said he had become a Christian," Rod said.

"Why? What did she say?"

"Well, she kept saying he was a Catholic, and I kept telling her there are a lot of Catholics and Baptists and

Presbyterians and all kinds of church people who aren't really Christians. That blew her mind, because I guess she thought anybody who went to a Christian church was a Christian."

"And you, of course, explained to her what a real Christian is?" Susie asked, laughing.

"Of course! She listened and found it very interesting. But you know what—what's happening with Pete will have more effect than everything I say to her," Rod said.

"We've really changed a lot in our year in California, haven't we?" Susie said.

Rod thought back to the day they arrived, and all that had happened since then. "Yeah—for the better I think, don't you?" he asked.

"Umm, I do."

They were happy. It had been a strange year, and they would never have another one exactly like it. But they also knew that their lives would never be the same again either.

QUESTIONS

Chapter 1

1. What religious emphasis first caught Rod's interest in his new community?
2. Based on information in this chapter, describe the religious character of Los Angeles.
3. List three bits of information you learned about Buddhism in this chapter.
4. Would you have reacted differently than Rod did to the Buddhist girl? If so, how?
5. Give your reaction to the way Rod answered Pete on the marijuana subject.

Chapter 2

1. What was the basis for Susie's reaction to the *Watchtower* article?
2. What religious faith did the couple Susie met at the laundromat have?
3. Describe the Buddhist group at worship.
4. What was the name of this particular branch of Buddhism?
5. List three things you learned about the Buddhist faith.

Chapter 3

1. What is a "Leaflet Missal"?
2. Briefly describe the Catholic worship service.
3. List three points of difference between Pete's faith and Rod's. List similarities.
4. What do you think of Rod's reaction to the way Pete worked with the boys?
5. Describe briefly how you would have handled it differently.

Chapter 4

1. What is a *seder?*
2. Briefly describe the *seder.*

3. W

4. H   servance
   of

5. D   e? If so,
   hc

1. Li   religious
   tre

2. D   sons.

3. H   a Chris-
   tia

4. Br   through
   th

5. In   er, show
   his

1. Wl   hip with
   Ro

2. Wl

3. Ho

4. Wl

5. Bri